To my friend John Povey

Smoke

and Other Tales

Published by
Lubin Publishing
Brune Street,
London E1
www.zerolubin.org

©2015 Lubin Publishing
All rights reserved

Printed and bound in Wales

First edition 2015

ISBN 978–0–9563077–7–4

MIX
Paper from
responsible sources
FSC
www.fsc.org
FSC® C010353

Printed by
Zenith Print Group
www.zenithprintgroup.com

Every reasonable attempt has been
made to identify owners of copyright.
Errors or omissions will be corrected
in subsequent editions.

Design: Louise Burston

Photographs by
Louise Burston and
Gerry King

Totnes postcard p42-43,
courtesy of John Hinde Collection Ltd.
www.johnhindecollection.com

Photograph on p58 courtesy of
Will Self, graphics by Louise Burston

London July 2015

Smoke
and Other Tales

~~GERRY KING~~

To Michael Surrealist Woods,
The real deal.
All the best

Gerry

Lubin Publishing
www.zerolubin.org

Contents

Foreword

'Denzel started to faze, like a digital station on a Bose radio.'
This aside, which comes near the end of Gerry King's
'Smoke', is at once typical of his writing – the uniting of a
liminal psychic event with an everyday object of great
specificity – and descriptive of his own method: There are
scores – nay hundreds – of images in this text that King
tunes into clarity and then fazes out into static and silence.
King's world is at once frozen into a series of defined time
periods and partakes of the curiously indeterminate
character of recency: the 1960s, 70s and 80s, when dedicated
followers of fashion still expressed taste through brand choices,
rather than a slavish adherence to commoditisation. These
washed-up boxers, English Riviera playboys, crystal-dependent
divas and tea-leafing, hypo-jockeying runners and riders are
the real fixative of our floating society – all that is solid,
Marx wrote in *The Communist Manifesto*, melts into air, but
in King's tales a residuum is left behind, a human stain, a
wheezing smirch, and that is life as it's truly lived.

Gerry King may, superficially, seem to be part of a long
tradition of such English sepia-to-noir chroniclers – scryers
of fire-resistant polystyrene ceiling tiles, readers of tea bags;
does he, perhaps, belong with Patrick Hamilton, Derek
Raymond and Julian MacLaren-Ross? Yes and no, because
King's perspective is at once more elegiac and more
imaginative than theirs: bedsit land is the launch pad, but up
there in the coffered heavens there are all manner of insights
to be discovered; about money and law and guilt and
transport and housing and redemption – about having and
losing and remembering that you never had it to begin with.

King's vision has the oblique prankishness of the great Russian Absurdist, Daniil Kharms, and the subversive sneakiness of Saki; and his fiction fuses the unexpected with damp carpet underlay.

For King, life presents as an endless series of moments – moments of poignancy, pathos and bathos, yet never, ever, of whimsy. His authorial eye discovers patterns in the dust motes lit up by the morning sunlight streaming through a toughened glass transom; he sees the quotidian spindrift float, light as thistledown, or else dust-devilling across the worn Axminster pile of the mind. There is no escape: we are what we eat and drink and smoke and shoot-up and drive and kiss and . . . And . . . when the time comes we put our memories on display, recollections like so many little souvenirs and curios, ready to be tipped unceremoniously on to that Axminster when the dodgy geezers arrive to cart the cabinet off.

Finally: what did you expect? What did you imagine life has in store for you? When they said there were no rehearsals, you still assumed there would be a press night: that there'd be an opportunity to hear the general reaction. But you know now, don't you: it's true, each event only happens once, each cigarette is only extinguished once. With the exception of Gerry King's rolled-up fiery treat of a book, which I urge you to light upon with your eyes again and again and again, because a smoke such as this one can always be relit.

Will Self, London, October 2014

Smoke: A Trilogy
The act of cleaning is primarily an act of erasure

PART ONE

The ashtrays waltzed out of beer gardens and seaside bars, hand bagged away from high-ceiling old-school pubs with acid-etched doors that advertised fine wines and brandies and snug saloon bars where Salvation Army sutlers peddled the *War Cry* like pious butlers. Holding the ashtray by the crust as the tar of forgotten fags was teased from sticky slopes and the detritus tipped into a carrier bag lined bin. Names of yore: Embassy, Watneys Red Barrel, Sterling, VAT 69, Mayfair, Johnny Walker and Players. The Craven 'A' badged circular glass ashtray waits for the next flicking and stubbing session in the centre of a marble-topped, cast-iron framed table, the type to fracture your skull in a bar room brawl. The light coloured marble displays a sporadic dull patination, evidence of acidic corroding spillage. A limestone psoriasis.

Even though I know the fate of the cowboy, I miss the regular Marlboro, particularly the smaller cigarette made for the American market: packed and punchy, each one tasting as good as the last. The esoteric Lark with charcoal filters, as smoked by Chas in *Performance* and the hard-hitting hand-rolling tobaccos of Drum and the long-gone Brown Beauty. Blue cigarette papers ensuing a rapid nicotine delivery system, the empty packets providing perfect roach material. Accoutrements: The clicking flick and flint grinding Zippo, the chromium American locomotive-like Ronson with the front loaded gas regulator and the chunky tooled gold night-clubbing Dunhill. The firing up, the inhalation, that dizzying first cigarette of the morning on a shared walkway with a strong breeze and a cityscape view. Fabulous plans for the day drawn from the burning stubby.

It is the tailor-made cigarette, factory manufactured and steeped in chemicals, that burns down in the ashtray like a fuse, as opposed to the hand rolled, with its fragrance of woodshed and hobbyist basement. Ready-made cigarettes leave an unpleasant legacy, entrenched in the fabrics and threadbare carpet of a claggy soiled and crowded bedsit. A film of nicotine covers the glass of an exhausted black coin-fed electricity meter, the lead and wire seal tampered with. Rolled newspapers retaining the stink, their twisted head-lines wet with condensation, are pressed into gaps in the wooden framed windows of a crumbling four storey Edwardian pile.

The fumigation, a smoking exorcism, an airing of the room, that second wind on a five-mile run, blown clear through. Give me all the things I take for granted; I want to live in a state of certainty and confident energy. Nip the glow, stub it out in a chromium Erhard spinning roulette ashtray as favoured by Greta Garbo, then wash thoroughly the forefinger and thumb. The sticking, juddery opening of a metal-framed window in a 1920s hotel near the English south coast, where the waved and frothed blown ozone will cleanse everything and make it fresh and bright again. Even my thoughts will be pure. I am enveloped with gratitude, recalling my first ever experience of ecstasy at the Club RoXY, Amsterdam circa 1989. Breathing in the expanse of an exotic pulsating Europe, the thin wooden spatula topping the bigheaded blonde beer that quenches my dancing thirst. My lungs will never be blackened-leather displayed like government health warnings on cigarette packets, because I know everything is clean and pink pure. A pharmaceutical stimulant, like the engine cleaner Redex, blows out the carbon build-up, smoothes the airflow and postpones the moment of inevitable decline.

In April 2014, it was announced in The Financial Times that Imperial Tobacco – owner of the Gauloises and Embassy brands – is to shut the last cigarette factory in mainland Britain. Closing factories in Nottingham and Nantes, France (where Imperial manufactured Gauloises cigarettes) will cost about nine hundred jobs in total. The Nottingham factory once produced one million cigarettes a day and employed up to seven thousand people.

PART TWO

Across the road from my tenement landing in Spitalfields are the luxury apartments of the Jewish Soup Kitchen. I can see this beautiful building from my front door of Carter House in Brune Street, East London. Designed by architect Lewis Solomon, the façade lends itself to the influence of the Art and Crafts movement. The building was completed in 1902, a decade before the Titanic went down. The street was then called Butler Street, changing to Brune Street in 1937. A line-pegged sari flaps against a London brick wall, marking the boundary of Holland Estate. The colourful material dances like a flag strung from the mast of an ocean-going tea clipper, crewed with lascars who spoil pet monkeys. There was talk of removing the wall and replacing it with railings in order to deter drug-dealing youths smoking their malodorous mañana-inducing skunk. Whilst this will facilitate a better airflow drying experience, the wall will be lost forever.

In 1998, while staying in Chicago, I was bitterly disappointed with the water quality of their launderettes, the fragrance and softness of my clothes brutalised. I suspected this was in the drying process. I remember reading somewhere that in 1938 the great Jesse Owens, the Olympic running champion, had opened a Chicago drive-in dry cleaners but it was not successful. I tried tumble-drying sheets without success. I know the line is best and aspire to the crisp freshness of white Egyptian cotton sheets over my shoulder as I remove new wooden pegs, purchased to avoid a curse.

The City creeps nearer to Spitalfields. I wonder if the facades of the new residential towers are clad with the same combustible thermoplastic that ignited in the United Arab Emirates, going up like Roman candles. The sealed steaming wombs of the tanked wet rooms, pulse showerheads with a 'lifetime' guarantee against limescale clogging. Twenty years – never a real lifetime – comparable to the shopping centres designed to last only a couple of decades. The annual cleaning contracts of these places are worth more than a provincial town's total budget: Ballardian Malls reminiscent of 1930s Singaporean casinos, pandering to low-level depression through therapeutic consumerism. I can visualise the sky through splayed fern fronds and wish for Los Angeles Queen Palms in parking areas lit by Stanley Kubrick. Brent Cross, a promised land where old time gangsters, once married to cheeky starlets, shoplift in Waitrose. Accompanied by their mothers, pouting black-haired Jewish princesses with French nails swan about holding smart phones as if modelling gloves.

In the numerous new residential apartments of the East End, history is bought in from the many 'We Saw you Coming' merchants, whose colourfully exaggerated personal backgrounds and foppish images are captured to sate the need of local historians for 'New Nostalgia.' The beaked myopic Blogging chroniclers are prepared to sell their own mothers for a *compos mentis* 'undiscovered' ninety-year-old living on Arnold Circus possessing an unseen family photograph album with cursive captions. This will be recorded in a vocabulary that melds Julian Maclaren-Ross with Enid Blyton, information that will translate effortlessly into a well-produced coffee table book archiving all our yesterdays. The walking marginalia of 'in living memory' becomes ever more dubious, with tenuous connections to individuals and events that cannot be verified. Over-coated tough guys brought up on tales of *'you could leave your doors unlocked'* recently attended the funeral of a gentleman thief buried in a wicker coffin. This was a refined affair, arranged by an artist and far removed from the clichéd black plumed horse cortèges when *'they only ever hurt their own.'* Authenticity is not a concern, as long as the material dovetails nicely with some celebrity trivia. Toynbee Hall in Commercial Street connects to Hull House, Chicago and Jane Adams. Historical facts and noble projects never get in the way of a good Ripper tour.

In the grimed dirt of the posh East End, Shoreditch House provides a British Harry's Bar, beauty treatments and networking facilities, because now everybody with a few bob is somebody. The nearby Box Park features shipping container shops spewing low-cal designer clothes, colour splashed gnomes, original art and candy-coloured headphones. Photo opportunities abound for first world hipsters – not to be onfused with the Ginsberg Angelheaded. Crisp, clear and clean, each shot just like another one, the recurring unoriginality of high-end technology. Street graffiti and a smattering of contrived local characters with their own chairs outside Bagel shops are rinsed out through the legions of lenses and flashes of iPod flaneurs. The street art aficionados know Blec Le Rat is the true master, while wanting a Banksy and not caring about his real name or what he looks like. New pasta shops open on Redchurch Street, run by refined Americans, all surgery white and bright with a reasonable lunchtime menu – for now – while sandwiches from Prêt a Manger are left on ledges for the homeless.

Hoxton beards, with girlfriends practising sulky resting bitch face, drink tea and tease kittens in Lady Dinah's Cat Emporium. Gentrification ripples smoothly out from the Bethnal Green Road end of the uber-fashionable Brick Lane. Gone is the DVD shop with posters of the Natural Born Killers, Mickey and Mallory, it's now a venture operated by Edwardian bearded twins flogging a choice of in excess of two hundred and fifty breakfast comestibles and fifteen different milks known as 'Cereal Killers.' Not so long ago, under the railway arches, working girls offered a 20 quid 'lick and suck': a hit on a crack pipe and oral sex. Now, the passing public are accosted by hipsteresses, outside the Truman Brewery, hawking nitrous oxide: *'laughing gas three pounds a balloon.'* In a minimalist warehouse pad, the shared experiences of false memory are enabled through the playing of a 1960s Bally pinball machine. No burning cigarettes tarring on the chrome and glass of this baby and the tilt an unwelcome thud – *steady now – it's vintage*! The Raleigh Chopper and bright orange space hopper sit in the fun reception of a Fashion Street advertising agency, trophies to a cool 1970s awareness somewhere between Hawkwind and David Bowie. Across from Commercial Street, the ghosts of the Brune Street Soup Kitchen might have been unsettled by their one-time basement dwelling resident, a city trader at UPS who was jailed for a £1.3 billion fraud, a market gamble that didn't pay off. The type of money that doesn't smell but attracts static, with purchasing power enough to swamp Switzerland in bread and herrings. There were in excess of a hundred elderly clients on the Kitchen's books when it closed in 1992.

Hand poured luxury scented candles disguise the smell of low-level fear directly proportional to market fluctuation. Property developers, wearing silk lined trousers that facilitate a fluidity of movement, personify a toxicity aligned to crystal meth smoke. Their wheeled suitcases and tyre-whispering Prius contribute to the neighbourhood sound-track. Holland Estate is boxed inside the boundaries of Bell Lane, Wentworth, Toynbee and Brune Street. These old school tenements were for people who worked with things you could hold, hoist, taste and smell. They will be cleared for massive investment opportunities; apartments that will look marvellous photographed with a fish eyed lens and captioned in a font with integrity. The minimum room size in the private housing sector was abolished in the 1980s; it is fabulous how you can touch the ceiling in some buildings. Purchasers are now paying for homes that Housing Associations would not build, with walls a crash helmeted American footballer could run through with swing ball hammer hands, screaming a line from *The Shining*, and a management company that never stops taking. *Because you are worth it.*

Leaving Smoke Daddy on West Division Street, taking the Chicago Skyway East into Gary, Indiana – the hum of industry still strong in the air. Once you could smell the oil in the

Turbine Hall of the Tate Modern, London – now it's more like Issey Myake. Gary, Indiana – crossing the State line to avoid Chicago City Tax on four cartons of stubby red Marlboro. United States Steel, with its four blast furnaces and 84-inch hot strip mill, looks out on Lake Michigan – waiting.

The eye line of the City is being redefined. From a penthouse perspective the uncomplicated order of buildings leads you always towards the City, with a nod to Shanghai. The landmarks remain; not quite the brutal Chicagoan redevelopment where short histories are erased (unless you want a tour of traditional pubs and housing estates), just a bit of an add on here and there such as the British Library or the Sainsbury's wing at the National Gallery. On Friday afternoons helicopters can be heard on rooftops over Bishopsgate way and they are not from the Barracks near Bunhill fields. A pub in Canary Wharf has sold for £32 million because the developers want to buy all the space in the sky and sunlight will be at a premium. Up through the atmosphere, up where the air is clear. Harry Flowers toasts the skyline with a large scotch: *'Here's to old England.'*

In Spitalfields abutment encroachment is the name of the game. The developers want to go up to the gods and their lift is stuck on the fourth floor. Foxes live in a row of semi-derelict shops along Toynbee Street, and will continue to do so unless the building regulations that specify the height of new buildings in this area are relaxed. *'Look after your partials'* a television advert warns: *'don't put a strain on your real teeth – take the strain off – glue your partial denture to your gums.'* Partial developments are going in now, prior to total implants that will shade whole streets. On the corner of Cobb Street and Bell Lane, a recent abutment is not sympathetic to the architecture of a small old shop selling big boxy suitcases and colourful wax print fabrics popular with Africans. Cunardesque in brutal stature, these brash interventions are a standard shade of washed out white. The street level floors swim with outdoor pursuit specialists and premium cycle shops. The scale of new next to old can be compared to Corgi and Matchbox toy cars – big toy, small toy. The original buildings are Matchbox, whose Lesley Product factory was once based at Hackney Wick, whilst the new, nautical-themed apartment blocks (more factory ships than trawlers) can be compared in scale to Corgi. *Look after your partials.* The new residents, more at home on a Blue Riband ocean-going liner than four floors up in the East End, have had the temerity to ask for a key to access the communal gardens of their social housing neighbours. Whole continents have been taken over in this manner and certainly not exclusively during the days of Empire. This hardnosed sense of entitlement flexes a pushiness that will get their offspring well placed and provide opportunities not based on ability: *But then that's life buoy, put it in your palm Olive.*

Crossing centuries, a vague context connects skilfully woven, washed and stretched cloth on the Tenterground at the corner of Brune Street, together with the appliquéd ransom note fonts on quilts and soft furnishings of an indulged woman/girl artist. The artist's sensitively restored three-floored London brick studio has a swimming pool in the basement. A roof garden edged with lavender to attract honeybees corrals exclusive limited edition printed deckchairs. All this is visible from the top of Whites Row Corporation of London multi-storey, soon to be demolished, car park.

Studding the old Spitalfields fruit and vegetable market are shops stacked high with many wants but few needs. Farrow & Ball painted emporiums purvey handbags, floaty things and age defying potions. Many of these shops exhibit items with no price tags, promoting the Curzonland ethos of 'if you have to ask the price, you can't afford it.' In a quaint, highly regarded, Northern writer's shop with a busy lunchtime trade, you have to ask the trendy and reassuringly refined assistant for the price of her oranges.

PART THREE

Two rooms of a first floor one-bedroom tenement flat in Carter House are economically carpeted, with no underlay, just thin foam backing. The carpet is covering paint-splattered 1970s lino tiles under which lay original pine planks imported from British Columbia. The hallway is now covered in recycled hardboard, stained black and polished, salvaged from the West End stage production of Stomp. The kitchen and bathroom, plus separate water closet, have black diamond patterned linoleum, caulked at the edges to contain seepage.

It is here that I daily apply first the moisturiser, then the ointment and finally the steroid cream. These lotions are applied to selective locations, my derma islands of trauma that sometimes drive me to momentarily satisfying scratch ing reminiscent of days of analgesic self-medication. Endeavouring to heal, cyclical treatments and then back to Portia Goldsmith consultant dermatologist for further encouragement and counsel in the matter of damage limitation, physically and mentally; one in ten afflicted with psoriasis will have suicidal thoughts. Wanting so much for it to clear and praying these isolated outbreaks do not join up; the partials must be kept in check.

My life has changed in so many ways but I have always been certain of the Rolling Stones. I may even have taken them for granted. I have never questioned Keith Richards' indestructibility; it is what I have expected of him. The passing of a Rolling Stone seems inevitable and I am sure, when this happens, it will solemnly affect me, even though I have never met or corresponded with a Stone. My Uncle Brian, a successful Californian-based businessman, once sat next to Bill Wyman flying first class across America.

My recent uncertainty began when a letter dropped through my front door informing me of an 'Intention to Demolish' the block of flats that I live in and the surrounding 3.5 acre Holland Estate. Dramatically, I played the Stones' live version of 'Gimme Shelter' recorded at Madison Square Gardens. Prior to the letter, I had been reading an article in *The New York Times* online about an exhibition by the French photographer Charles Marville being held at the Metropolitan Museum of Art, recording the 'Haussmannisation' of Paris. The term was named after Baron Georges-Eugene Haussmann, a Seine Prefect who was instrumental in the modernisation of Paris. The duality of the Parisian redevelopment from 1853-70, the clearing of the slums, the building of boulevard's too wide to successfully ever barricade. The relocation of the lower orders to the peripheries, going orbital and waiting for the brave new world of Charles-Édouard Jeanneret-Gris AKA Corbusier. I wondered who will be waiting for me if I am decanted to outer Stratford, the sterile hell of the Olympic park or beyond.

Carter House in Brune Street has been my home for a number of years. I have grown to love the distinctive London

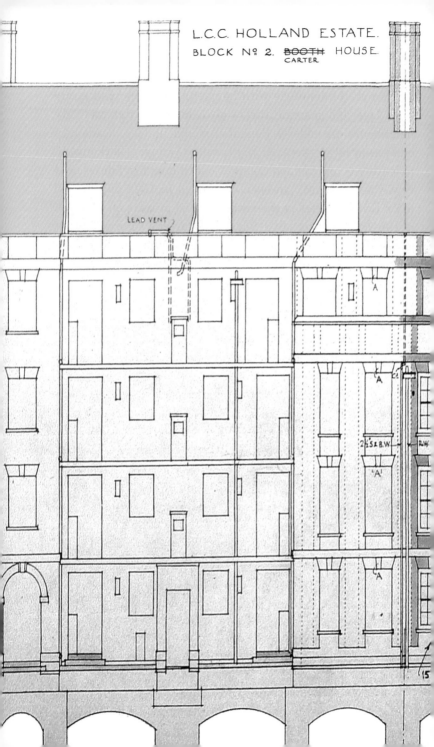

L.C.C. HOLLAND ESTATE.

BLOCK Nº 2. ~~BOOTH~~ CARTER HOUSE.

LEAD VENT

A

A

A

2½S₁ B.W.

"A"

R.W.

A

5

brick, the black hatched rubbish chutes that match the railings and handrails, the historically oil-stained concrete stairs and the landings with homegrown money plants; my olive tree and jasmine thrive on a bin area flat roof. My neighbours are elderly Bengalis, media luvvies, academics and essential workers. At the London Archive, Clerkenwell, in leather-bound London County Council minutes, I discovered that Carter House had been completed in 1928 and named after Ernest Carter, a vicar who had led prayers on the deck of the *Titanic* as it sank. Reverend Carter's Church was St Jude's, just around the corner on Commercial Street; St Jude being the patron saint of the Chicago police department and lost causes.

This extremely disconcerting missive arrived in a regular envelope, popped casually through my grey primer-concealing mahogany front door with its polished brass letterbox. The wording of letters such as these have no doubt been honed over the years; political parties bickering over trivia, while corporate lawyers continually developed their muscles, flexing, smooth and subtle. The lessons were learnt from previous conquests, the leaseholders no doubt consulting solicitors, the opening dinner party topic and fingering their calculators. I don't own my home but I have a tenancy agreement that is old school and I could and will name a successor to my flat. Obviously conditions will apply, probably within the context of assistance in my advancing years. These are the rights that the swiftly developing want to eradicate as it 'complicates matters.'

Alluding to the victualing practice of wines, the residents will be decanted, their right to acquire or buy suspended, possibly for at least five years. There is stipulation within housing association policy that tenants cannot acquire anything above a valuation of £320,000; this figure will easily be surpassed during the period of suspension. The council tax property bands, based on fresh valuations, will rise on the new developments substantially. Residents cannot buy or acquire their property and must wait to be priced out of their homes. Leaseholders will probably be offered 20% over market value; maybe some tricksy buy back might be negotited. There are elements of Alistair Cooke and his *Letters From America*. Mr. Cooke lived in an apartment overlooking Central Park in New York City. He stated that, in his later life, this was only possible through rent control; the low percentage of market rent enabled his residency into his final years.

Five years, is that all we've got? The served notice mentioned a five-year time span. Edgar, an Eastend Homes Housing Officer whom I count as a friend, had told me: *'they are going to make an offer we can't refuse'*, nodding towards the City from a tenement block near Middlesex Street. This is from a man fluent in French and with more than a passing interest in the legacy of the banlieue. His own parents came to London from Ghana in the late 1950s, their residing locations a dead cert – not possible now. It is certain that an offer has been made and there won't be a whisper of a 1939 Chamberlain ditherer. Boardroom Panzer commanders will blow me out of my gaff, their Tiger Tank attire, a mix of linen and silk. Bulleted Mont Blancs will sign documents that will demolish the buildings Goering's bombs fortuitously missed.

On a whim, I went across the road and rang the doorbell of a top floor flat in the Jewish Soup Kitchen. A woman spoke to me through the intercom and I explained the situation with regards to the letter. She was not surprised and I asked if I could take a photograph from her facing windows. She buzzed me up and kindly allowed me to get a different perspective of my home from a protected view.

Psoriasis is a hereditary skin condition. It can be exacerbated by stress; however, there are other triggers and over-compensation presides at its core. I was washing a wooden sash window frame in my father's Torquay flat with sugar soap, preparing the paintwork. I don't think he ever smoked in the bedroom but it needed a few coats to enliven the space. Standing on a small 'A' frame wooden ladder, I stepped back and my foot went through a rotten floorboard, scraping my shin; this was the trigger. Normal skin cells mature and replace dead skin every 28-30 days, but psoriasis causes skin cells to mature in less than a week. The body cannot shed old skin and the unsightly legacy is scaly patches of dead skin on the arms, back, chest, elbows and legs. Following the Liverpool pathway, I watched my father die over a four-day period, his psoriasis clearing up as his body closed down.

A prayer to St Jude:
Saint Jude worker of Miracles
pray for us
Saint Jude helper and keeper of the hopeless
pray for us.
Thank you Saint Jude.

Time

Considering time, there are certain combinations of numbers that are not striking in a visual or a spoken manner; for example, 3.39 a.m. does not command attention. However, 2.30 a.m. has a certain ring to it. As for midnight, it doesn't even have to try – hands up like a numerical ballet performed by Merce Cunningham, praising the darkness for all manner of possibilities, trysts, tricks, trauma, black taxi travel and an hour over the late rate.

Steady time-consuming distractions are the online rolling news bulletins, continually updating and tantalisingly embellishing as relationships and associations are revealed. An example of a story I let steal my time was the hunting of an armed man in a remote area of the north of England. The public unravelling of a once unexceptional life. The scrutiny of the sock drawer and the glove box; television footage of his home depicting an unkempt garden, a few toys peeping out of the grass and a white painted local authority gate not quite closed.

The news stated he was living in a tent and recording lengthy Dictaphone messages outlining thoughts and grievances. These tapes were found by his pursuers and examined for clues. The censored morsels served up for Argos catalogue readers to devour while broadsheet subscribers remembered *Emmerdale Farm* from their student days. I found myself considering the logistics of an incident such as this. Points of archaic reference entered the frame, such as Geoffrey Household's *Rogue Male* and elements of *The 39 Steps*. Clipped English and whistling steam trains accompany *Withnail* in a barren rain-lashed cottage.

Spalding Gray used a Dictaphone with an earpiece to deliver his lines at The Performing Garage in New York City circa 1980. He drowned in the Hudson River almost 25 years later. This time, the conclusion was nearer *Get Carter* than Alexander Trocchi's tugboat location. Sitting cross-legged in the rain with his back to a river, the hunted northern man blew his brains out with a sawn-off shotgun.

I remember an early 1980s news item recording the suicide of a barman killer who was on the run, holed up in the back of a Bedford CF van in Earls Court. It was established he was under the influence of stimulants. I try to relate to his indescribable paranoia, a vanned and skint Tony Montana. I wonder how his waking nightmare took him, who said what and who had the last word in his sparking brain. What happened to the van? I knew a girl whose brother worked in a scrap yard. She told me that the fire brigade would hose down the motors brought in from motorway death crashes and the scrap yard dogs would clean up what was left of the bloody residue. I doubted this story – surely they would shred their paws on sharp metal edges?

I think of individuals in areas of colossal upheaval world-wide. I imagine how their time is passing in situations of incredible duress: hungry, wet and cold on a mountainside, men down mines or cast adrift on vast oceans, waiting to be found or waiting for death. The scale of time must pass differently, the thoughts and distractions in diverse tongues but the feelings still the same. The extremity of the situation: life as survival, not a choice of American donuts or a sun bed warning. For a while and not for long enough, I get a real perspective. I have made pledges with a credit card and trusted that maybe something changed for someone somewhere, that their time was made easier.

Grand Charity Night

IN AID OF THE MENTALLY HANDICAPPED

*

Sponsored Boxing Tournament

Wednesday, 26th March

1980

at 7.30 p.m.

*

PALM COURT HOTEL
TORQUAY

*

ADMISSION PROGRAMME £1.50

20 Two-Minute Rounds

The Herald Express is a provincial newspaper predominantly covering Torbay in Devon. In the late 1970s, it was broadsheet. On the cover, there used to be a late news section running down the right hand side. If the paper was purchased at lunchtime from a vendor who hawked them round the harbourside pubs, this section was empty. It was here that my father Paul King and his drinking pals, mostly the unconventional self-employed, would make up their own news in biro. The main subjects were usually who wasn't paying their round, domestic disputes and nice little earners that involved copperised milk churns and 'original' prints framed from books. Sometimes world events inspired a mention. These creative writing classes would invariably occur in The Royal Vic, The Queens or The Hole in the Wall.

HUF 126E, a gunmetal grey 4.2 Jaguar, crouches at the curb while Paul King strikes a fighting pose outside 47 Warbro Road for *The Herald Express* photographer. You either put up or shut up. Stay cool and look mean. Hold that pose on the toes of an old pair of baseball boots; dark heavy cotton tracksuit bottoms with a few paint stains.

It's all about numbers. March 26th, 1980: Paul King, The Torquay Tornado, will fight 20 two-minute rounds in the ballroom of the magnificent seafront 'Queen of the English Riviera', Palm Court Hotel in Torquay. This boxing exhibition will hopefully raise £500 to purchase exercise equipment for the mentally and physically handicapped adults Paul works with at a local hospital. Attractive ringside bikinied girls are to announce the rounds on numbered boards and a cabaret will fracture the performance in a showbiz fashion.

Paul King is 48 years old and enjoys a drink, a few cigars and a cavort. Paul believes that as long as he doesn't drink more than his doctor, he's okay. His doctor, who has something of the Nigel Havers about him, is Peter Rovira; he also enjoys a drink and is a charmer. He will be in Paul's corner on fight night and right up until the end of his life. Paul has convinced Peter he will be fine, on the basis that 'Old Mongoose', aka Archie Moore, one time light heavyweight champion of the world, didn't retire from the ring until he was 47 years old.

22 years from the barking MC announcing seconds out, the glory days of the smoky halls and arenas, dancing on canvas, punch like a rivet gun. Paul knows the score and this is his way to enter a final chapter of his life. It's all a bit of fun unless you wanted to make it something else. A truly noble mid-life crisis that does not involve a Harley Davidson, a Thai bride or hair dye.

Hankie Trilogy

Mummy's Boy
Blood Sweat and Tears
The Mantle of the Dandy

Mummy's Boy

James Brown sang '*It's a Man's, Man's, Man's World*' but it didn't feel like that when my mum would wet the corner of her lily-of-the-valley perfumed, lipstick stained, lace-edged handkerchief and rigorously remove chocolate from the corners of my mouth.

All this would take place in my uncle George's motorcycle sidecar while he thundered, resplendent with a red polka dot neckerchief, through the gloaming of the 1960s streets of Battersea.

Blood, Sweat and Tears

If you watch the classic 1950 Otto Preminger noir thriller, *Where the Sidewalk Ends,* filmed on the rain-slicked streets of New York, it is evident that only the main players benefit from the use of a handkerchief: a prop as important as a skull in a Shakespearian tragedy.

During a heated exchange involving the issue of police brutality, the corrupt cop, played by Dana Andrews, utilises a neatly folded handkerchief to wipe blood from a cut eye, while his Chief of Detectives pulls a billowing handkerchief from his pocket to mop the sweat from his brow.

The beguiling beauty, Gene Tierney, is the love interest and in a scene of high drama that nearly leads to a kissing episode, she breaks into racking sobs that only abate when she gently dabs the tears from her eyes with a dainty handkerchief.

The Mantle of the Dandy

Clive the Poodle Faker effortlessly picks up the mantle of the dandy and gives it a 21st Century revamp.

The constant accessory that transcends time is the handkerchief. Once pouched effeminately from a ruffled wrist, Clive now encourages the brightly coloured silk to hang tantalisingly from his blazer pocket. His favourite handkerchief is a silk map of Europe that his uncle once concealed in his flying boot during Lancaster sorties over Germany.

Clive sometimes likens himself to a scene William Macy plays in the American film *Magnolia*. He believes he has so much love to give.

Throwing the Toys Out of the Pram

The incident, conceivably as obtuse as the event featuring Judi Dench's late husband, Michael Williams on the balcony in Caracas, occurred on the High Street, Totnes within close proximity of the Brutus Stone.

The gleaming black Silvercross Regency Coach pram with sweeping body mouldings and hand painted gold details was being mummy-steered up the pavement, when the possibly life-changing incident happened. The baby was not Bambi harnessed with a serrated edged and felt strapped accessory and in a moment of careless window-shopping he falls head-first from the pram striking the pavement with his still-forming cranium. The child was swooped up, bosom-held and head kissed. The black 22-inch Morlands adjustable fringed canopy with little cream doves was then pushed down to enable a sleeker, faster conveyance to the chemist. It was said the bump on baby's head was the size of an egg but there was never a mention of an x-ray or a doctor's visit. The catalyst for the following perspective could possibly be attributed to this unfortunate incident that occurred decades previously. Strong elements of the lawnmower joke, a joke that cannot be revealed, are evident in this journey.

Totnes. It does have a special place at the dinner party, catering to the more acerbic cultural cognoscenti for its refined traits of all-inclusivity and celebration of diversity, nimbyism and being the bastion of well-educated dysfunctional malarkyists with their handmade shoes, knitted scarves and vacuous smiles. There is something extremely self-seeking and unpleasant about the town; an ersatz idyll feeding off an ethos hijacked from the 1920s legacy up the road at Dartington. Many years ago, a pal of mine told me about a hotel near Coatbridge in Scotland where, if you were a *bona fide* salesman, you could get a drink at any time. But you had to be a *bone fide* salesman. Dartington College of Arts did provide Totnes with some credentials. Without Dartington College lending creative integrity, it has been commented that Totnes has now lost its edge.

The salt-of-the-earth born and bred Totnesian is becoming the residual Cockney of Tower Hamlets. These are solid folk who remember the days when you could hear the pigs squealing from the Plains as they were slaughtered at the Harris bacon factory. It is as if a community has been hijacked by an insipid privileged power promoting a Narnian Sharia law. Internet connections blocked for selfish reasons masquerading as health concerns. Affluent outsiders braying how they bring employment to the area – usually a cleaner. Art-sponsoring solicitors who abhor social housing rub along with the war photography tourists dining out on tales of danger as their self-righteous damage is soothed in the natural beauty of the South Hams. While the names on the war memorial are forgotten, the well read march up the High Street protesting against conflicts that will never affect them.

Rich incomers have been known to bring tragedy through their self-seeking behaviour, desperately trying to impose their Bowling Green mentality on a Dartmoor gorse vista. There is the tale of the outlying pig farmer, a man of diminishing means whose only fiscal salvation was placed in expansion. He had acquired the planning permission and the conditional loan, but the newly arrived residents objected, hurling city-bought resources at this man losing his livelihood and, it transpired, his wife. The money won; the failed farmer parked in front of their home and gassed himself in his car. The objectors departed soon after. But it's their party and they will buy if they want to. A woman who owns a bed shop was overheard saying that the cold weather would be an excellent way to clear the homeless out of Totnes. There have been high profile money feuds written on hearses and celebrated by local bands. Totnes as Lumberton, USA with the guns removed and Frank Booth living at The Grosvenor Hotel in Torquay.

In the many bespoke high-street premises, the savouring of every moment enhances the civilised shopping experience. Everyday interactions are elevated through eye contact and winsome smiles, leisurely discussing the probable seasonable contents of the organic vegetable boxes paid for through *à la mode* Amway type schemes or the trusted vitamin supplement scams perpetrated on trusting friends and neighbours.

The town has more than its fair share of middle-aged men with painful pasts preying on lonely and dispossessed females in a uniquely Totnesian fashion. When questioned, regarding improper touching, these shadows of Max Cady will claim they were performing a manual lymphatic drainage massage. Oh yes, the shadow dancers, talking salad and eating chocolate. Healing blocked emotions and straightening out those pain loops. An almost psychotic smile masks the ecstasy-saturated psyche where anger leaches out . . . privately. The esoteric knowledge of the plausible − standing many of them in good stead in the

'alternative' field as counsellors. The local 'Iron John' male bonding group that smacks of naked grappling prior to campfire confessions and healthy dawn erections, is run by a 'geezer' in recovery from an addiction, which served to give him an identity, prior to discovering that his familial historical criminality could contribute nicely to his kudos. He then published a creative autobiography that was well received by liberal reviewers of self-help books.

Self-sufficient fading beauties with floppy elbows and Dennis Waterman replacement teeth, tell tales of international dalliances with well-known rock stars. These women, now purveyors of vintage clothing, antiques and crystals, drive French diesels displaying tattered 'Free Tibet' and Glastonbury stickers. Crumpled egg boxes, crushed Evian bottles and jump leads litter the passenger foot well. Woody old favourites such as drug and alcohol issues are considered passé; the new kids on the block are sex addiction, eating disorders and allergies. Regressive hypnotherapy reveals Celtic Kings and Queens keeping their dreams alive shelf-stacking at Morrison's, while others teach part-time yoga in Scandinavian-style extensions on farms bought with the proceeds of 1970s dope smuggling. Tarot readings are performed for people between relationships or Ashburton and Buckfastleigh. The numerous empowerment workshops endorsed by bipolar celebrities are heavy with integrity, appealing to a gathering of lost souls seeking spiritual landscapes within which to retreat.

Totnes is fabulous in the enablement of the new age charlatans and the trustafarian ne'er-do-wells. Often big fish motor in, spreading largesse until they rat themselves out through past ligger behaviour, dastardly domestic abandonment or dishonest business dealings. Towns like Brighton, bold enough to host Julie Burchill and Nick Cave, are straightforward in their decadence and dealings – you know the score. Totnes however is illusory, having a 'special thing' – akin to 'our little secret' going on under the Boden and Barbour. Sex on the East Sussex groynes would certainly beat louche kissing within the precinct of the Norman Motte and Bailey castle.

Sometimes, Always, Never

Reggie is a skilled tailor. The nature of bespoke tailoring is solitary and, in his seclusion, Reggie crafts Italian wool, fine gabardine twill or heavy Harris tweed while considering the complementary merits of a wide gamut of silk linings and buttons.

Reggie explains the etiquette of button fastening to me. Starting with the top button he says: '*Sometimes.*' Pointing at the second: '*Always.*' Then the last: '*Never.*'

I like the sense of order in Sometimes, Always and Never.

And in the End

Midday in early April 2008 finds me looking for a nursing home for my dad. I arrive unannounced at a double-entranced white villa in a beautiful part of Torquay. I later discover this palatial building has historical connections to Lillie Langtry. I meet the matron and four hours later I leave. Within a week my dad is living there, waking with a view across the bay.

Prior to this, Dad had been living alone for nearly eighteen months and not coping too well. My stepmother, Paula, had already been taken into a nursing home. Dad told me Paula burned out two clutches on the Ford Focus that he himself was to roll over a year later on his birthday. I thought Paula was different, there was young girl jollity about her, like a Tennessee Williams Southern Belle. I sent a spray of flowers to her from John Lewis for Christmas, enclosing a card, telling her I loved her and that she had always been like a mother to me, buying me warm clothes for birthday and Christmas presents. Paula never received the spray or the card as she was admitted to the nursing home a week before Christmas. Dad thought she would come home but she never did, and their little nest fell apart from December 2006 onwards.

Their home was, as always, welcoming, bright and spotless. Paula took great pride in the little touches, like the small bouquet of silk flowers in a fluted wall vase above the telephone table. I remember the glass curio cabinet filled with small treasures and keepsakes from foreign holidays, the extending table and chairs with padded lime-green ribbed seats and a comfortable three-piece floral suite corralling a long glass coffee table. On the coffee table, alongside a cut-glass bowl filled with liquorice allsorts, was a wooden cigar box carved with a boxing glove and my dad's name. On the walls were his prints and pictures and photos of Paula's nieces.

I would occasionally stay in the snug spare room with mirror-fronted wardrobes, filled with boxing memorabilia. I'd read myself to sleep, usually with books by old boxers, self-published, signed by the authors with a dedication to my dad. I would often take Paula and Dad a cup of tea in the morning, placing the cups on their matching bedside cabinets. The Jarman and Platt bedroom suite was cream with gold trimmings; the wardrobe had little porcelain panels painted with flowers.

After Paula died, I'd go and visit Dad, clean up and cook a meal, but everything was falling apart. Here was a man not used to looking after himself, drinking too much and smoking too many cigars. A chip-pan fire, a bad leg getting worse, spillages, domestic appliances breaking down; Dad broke down and went into hospital. Time had taken its toll. I would tell Dad that Mick Jagger was still performing and there was only fourteen years between them. Dad would reply that Mick Jagger hadn't had his life. I learnt the differences between residential and nursing care, and the funding implications. My perception of time changed. It wasn't the filmic flipping calendars with numbers and dates blowing away to oscillating strings. I made time brutal: violent in its intent. This was not the fault of time of course, it was I who had taken time for granted. One day, Dad said to me: 'Last night I dreamt I could run again, fast and easy.

Then I woke up and felt my stiff, useless knee.' He looked at me wide-eyed and resigned, then smiled and said, '*I like the flying dreams best. At least when I wake up, I know where I stand.*'

I would take Dad out in my old black diesel Saab. He would be hoisted from his wheelchair on to the covered front seat and we would motor up to an exclusive area with stunning views of the South Devon coastline, where, as Dad would always remind me, Max Bygraves had lived. Looking out over the bay, huge oil tankers were playing for time, waiting for prices to go up or the weather to calm down. I would always make Dad a bottle of brandy and water, a plastic one with a pop-up stopper. Sometimes, he couldn't get a firm grip, so I'd give the bottle a good squeeze, which he appreciated. We had stopped using glasses as he kept dropping them and my car was beginning to smell like a pub. I especially remember blustery winter days when we would sit listening to a Roy Orbison and Cat Power CD compilation. Dad particularly liked the track *Lived in Bars* by Cat Power. I noticed, on the cover of her CD *The Greatest*, a pair of gold boxing gloves hangs from a gold chain. Dad would lift his right hand, cigar between his fingers, and like Johnny Shannon in the Nic Roeg film *Performance*, he'd say: '*I like that, son, turn it up.*' It wasn't so much the words of the song; it was the sentiment we both shared.

Those billowing, rain-lashed days reminded me of the weather in South Wales and walking in the Black Mountains with the artist Roger Cecil. Roger was ten years younger than my dad but I remember his resilience and determination, and I wanted some of it for Dad. I wanted him to walk again. But that was never going to happen. Dad's cigar would go out and he'd ask

me to light it. I'd take the sodden cigar from him and feel like a bad son and a selfish bastard for resenting his spittle. I always checked his stoma bag before we went out and made sure his nails were kept clean and cut. You can't get sentimental over nursing home care; I always kept my eye on the ball. I could never have imagined that these things would happen. But life goes on until one day it calls time. I knew that Dad wasn't going to resist going 'gently into that good night' this time. He wasn't raging against anything any more. I could sense his tiredness and that's why we would sit quietly together, letting nothing stressful into our orbit. I assured him he had nothing to worry about, that everything was okay and all was well.

I had been at my dad's bedside with his sister Edna, my auntie, for over four days. She had flown into Heathrow on one of the last planes from the States before the volcanic ash hit. Time took on a routine, rotational pace: resting, reading, handholding, brow-wiping, lip moistening, looking at photograph albums. Edna and I would exchanges stories and there were revelations for both of us. We both realised it was just a matter of time. There was not going to be any miraculous recovery, this was the end. I fetched fragrant candles, flowers and odour neutralisers to mask the smell of death in the room.

My dad passed away at 4.45 a.m. on Wednesday 21st April, 2010. I showered and changed my clothes, putting on a pair of his casual trousers that had his room number written with indelible ink on an inside pocket. Edna and I talked, cried and laughed; then it was time for her to go. Dust cloud restrictions were lifted and she flew out on one of the first planes to the States the following day. It was a beautiful sunny morning as he was shushed away from the bright white Victorian villa. In a long black car, he passed through silent streets with occasional palm trees, to the undertaker's premises that had been his local newsagents years before. I remember my mum had always bought the *Daily Mirror* there and I would get my NME. Later, on my way to the undertakers to sort out arrangements, I met Paul the Continental Hairdresser, who was out getting his newspaper. I told him Dad had passed away that morning and he let out a string of expletives, running his hand through his magnificent bouffant grey hair.

Weeks later, I was reading an article about an artist who had created a piece of work using clips from films that, either in the script or the image, referred to a specific time. This twenty-four hour film in real time is potentially endless. The artist had mentioned that the lead-up to midnight was intense, whereas the hardest time to cinematically fix was 5.00 a.m. I thought about all the unconventional hours I had spent in my dad's company.

In the early 1970s, when Dad worked at The Carlton Club, I would help the chef in the kitchen, making up prawn cocktails and Melba toast. The chef and I would watch the cabaret from behind the glass-fronted cooler counter fridge. A resident band provided the backing music for a variety of singers and entertainers, including a belly dancer and numerous comedians. I remember a couple called Steve and Bonnie, who played guitar and sang. Steve had long blonde hair and Bonnie was black, with a superb Afro. The club hours were 8.00 p.m. till 2.00 a.m. Some nights, after closing time, I would go with Dad for meals at Greek restaurants or to parties on the beach or in rented bungalows in Paignton.

Bow ties skew-whiff, fighting poses with pals, banter such as 'Careful, I'm delicate.' Driving home along the seafront, a beautiful railway poster morning, the sun hot on the vinyl seats of the column change Ford Corsair, the 'Walrus of Love', Barrence Eugene Carter, playing on the eight-track. Years later, on Sunday mornings, still half-cut from the night before, we would park up, waiting for the 12 o'clock pubopening, listening to Derek and Clive, the irrational alcoholic laughter, tears running down our faces: father and son in a scene a southern Shane Meadows has yet to capture. Over the limit, over-emotional, yet knowing that time was significant.

When the time came, I dipped my finger into the powder that was once Dad and scattered his ashes at a spot where we had always parked and looked out over the bay, listening to music. Barry White to Chan Marshall. The endearments, the threats, the empty promises and well-intentioned grandiosity are now just words on a page. I have thought about my dad a great deal since he passed away in April 2010. Sometimes these thoughts are sentimental, but sometimes I selfishly search for clues as to my character. I wonder how well I knew my dad. I believe the last three years of his life were the years when we were closest. I took a renewed interest in his glory days and shared his memories. I wanted to understand him more and make sense of the past and celebrate it in my future. I know he had regrets about my mother, Greta; he told me this. He often asked me if he had been a good father. I always said yes.

In the Neighbourhood

The pony-tailed, middle-aged performance poet with a widow's peak and a small crucifix hanging from his earring, holds court to an audience of school-location-savvy NHS managers, trust fund creatives and self-employed genteel builders with artistic affectations. The usual pleading in sing-songy verse and gesticulation that takes those of a certain age back to a sad place somewhere between Gary Glitter and Morrissey, sans tinsel or gladioli. After a few desperately predictable verses struggling to achieve street credibility, it is rudely apparent poetry is not the new rock'n'roll. Certainly not tonight. The 'act' is fragrantly married to a woman who fabulously matches his pretensions. Some wits have commented it is a marriage made in envy.

Members of the audience nod like parcel-shelf dogs basking in the knowledge that their pensions, buy-to-let portfolios and bequests from soon-to-die-parents, will keep them at a safe distance from a generation that can only dream of paid university fees, full grants and jobs for life. The Saturday *Guardian* and cafétière on the oiled hardwood table with a calico canvas umbrella tapping into the inner colonial, *in spite of yourself*. The paved plot of garden, fig tree and lavender in pots all playing the part.

Present at this small launch party in a Real Ale pub, whose landlord has a strong connection to 1980s bands and edgy comedians, is the local publisher. An old hand – a subsidised man. Floppy covered books that friends will buy but no one will read. The publisher has refined a self-deprecating guffaw, finger pointing out from top lip, hand nearly fisted, accompanied with a little jig. Plenty of 'old times' sake' and five-pint bonhomie here tonight, in a neighbourhood gentrified at the price of an early 1970s compulsory purchase for a ring road that never happened.

The singleton ladies, who wisely bought their two-up two-down terraces in the late 1990s, their racy youth now gone like a 1975 Jensen Interceptor, while the legacy of excess remains. The depressives, over-eaters and self-harmers trying to bury modern madness under desk-based hobbies and expensive therapy, while blowing lint from their bare floorboards treated with linseed. A smattering of recovering addicts who missed the boat and blame everyone else for their bad time-keeping; applying for council, probation and housing careers based on subjective experience and a sense of wanting to belong. The chronic alcoholic entrenched in a thirty-year-old tragedy, who doesn't drive but bought a caravan on a bender. The caravan was delivered, wheels bricked, parked facing down one of the steepest streets in Europe. However, the street is not officially recorded as a thoroughfare.

The Bachelor Bicyclette Brothers

The annual Dauphiné Libéré cycle race would always feature the Bachelor Bicyclette Brothers heavily dosed on Delysid – their handlebars accommodating convex mirrors to enhance the experience.

The Stealerant: What's in a Name?

Names. What's in a name? John from Derby had a habit of pulling a single hair from his head and tickling his nostrils or ears while talking softly in a nasal manner with occasional sniffles. He was good at crosswords and, in a glancing moment, nailing the essence of someone in a nickname. Eddie and John were sitting in a Seven-Up signed café with a blue No. 6 cigarette sticker in the window and within earshot of a Gottlieb Pin Table, pushed beyond tilt for the thump of a replay. The hissing name-badged hot water Still, stamped with a royal crest, steamed into a stainless steel teapot. The wooden drawer till, with its dirty brass handle, tinkled feebly and the tomato sauce bottles, crusted round their screw necks, were cut with vinegar. John and Eddie were enjoying a fried breakfast with a slice and a mug of tea: the most important meal of the day, setting you up, filling the tank and lining the stomach.

John had managed to get from a Buddhist monk to Eddie's new moniker between two pieces of sausage and a slither of finned mushroom, via a week-old *Sunday Times* magazine taken from his doctor's waiting room. He pointed at a page titled *The Self-Immolation of a Buddhist Monk*. *'See that?'* John asked, *'rapid transportation to the afterlife through accelerant; but you don't see the petrol – d'you know what I mean?'* Eddie considered the image: *'No I don't.'* John continued: 'Extreme examples Eddie, from here to there quickly, like pieces put through auctions, lifted or liberated as you describe them.' Eddie had once remarked that the majority of antiques had been stolen at least once. As a fruit machine coughed dough into a trough, John rolled up the

WARNING

MENU

DRINKS
LARGER £2·50
SOFT DRINKS £1·00
TEA £1·00
COFFEE £1·50

SMALL LARGE
DONER   £4·00   £6·00
CHICKEN SHISH £4·50   £6·00
KOFTE   £4·00   £6·00
CHICKEN BURGER £4·00 £4·00
(MADE)
NUGGETS × 7   £5·00
        × 7   £5·00

SALAD PITTA   £3·50
HUMUS SALAD   £3·50
CHIPS   £2·00
CHIPS PITTA   £2·50
CHIPS + CHEESE   £3·00

ROLLS
EGGS ROLL £2·00
BACON ROLL £2·50

ALL ARE WELCOME

ENGLISH BREAKFAST

ALI'S

magazine and reached over the table, lightly touching Eddie on each shoulder. With solemn eye contact, he whispered nasally: '*You shall from this time be known as The Stealerant.*' Eddie laughed, '*Yeah and you still owe me three amps.*' This was a reference to the physeptone ampoules, which John as a registered addict, received through a prescribing consultant psychiatrist who incidentally lived with his mother and was an alcoholic.

John was not really a practical man. Eddie recalled an incident late one night in the multi storey car park in Torquay when three women were standing around a car which had a flat tyre. The women had been to Bingo in Temperance Street and had driven from Wales. Eddie offered to change the wheel, but realised John had no idea what to do. Eddie knew how to change a wheel because he had watched his dad do it, but it was probably a good bet that John had never had anyone there for him as a plug wiring or omelette making role model when he was a kid. The character of Chauncey Gardener played by Peter Sellers in the film *Being There*, the boy/man with no practical experience, reminded Eddie of John, whose life skills had been acquired from various government institutions. He devoured paperbacks, always paperbacks, such as Luke Rhinehart's *Dice Man and Shadow of the Cobra: The Life and Crimes of Charles Sobhraj*, a hippy trail serial killer of the 1970s. Released from jail, on the out, John would spend afternoons in near empty cinemas with a box of Maltesers and ten Piccadilly. He had also developed an interest in Native American Indians, not unusual amongst amphetamine users.

A most fortuitous happening involved the duplication of Derby John's script, due to a fictitious pressing engagement in London. It was first collected from the pharmacy at Torbay hospital, while Alex the taxi driver waited outside in his yellow 244 Volvo estate, and again three days later from Halls, Shaftesbury Avenue in the west end of London. Exactly how this repetition was achieved has been lost in the mists of time. Everything was drugs and money; all significance goes back to drugs and money. On this well trampled track, there was an element of 'Jerusalem Syndrome', where random images and objects are imbued with religious meaning and significance. Legacy and trace. Only it isn't about legacy and trace; it's about being embedded.

An Everett glass and chrome 2 ml syringe, the barrel filled with a rich honey gold liquid. The opening bars of Frank Sinatra's 'Under my Skin', live at the Sands in Las Vegas with Count Basie and his Orchestra, arranged by Quincy Jones. Looking sharp and slowly selling off all the nice pieces, the Cartier tank watch with semi-precious stones and the Mappin and Webb ashtrays and lamp stand. A passing thought tucked away in a rush. However, real life goes on and on. Maturity or death.

Eddie the Stealerant would miss John when, four years later, he heart-brokenly hanged himself with his own belt in the grounds of a psychiatric facility tendering doubtful drug rehabilitation services through a methadone reduction regime. The daily house meetings, classified as group therapy, usually descended into chaos and long days were spent smoking and listening to scratched Pink Floyd and Noel Coward records in the recreation room. John, on his institutional manoeuvres, had fallen in love with an ex of Roger the Rat Boy. The woman was rail thin, black haired and a worshipper of tubercular French poets in an infantile unresearched fashion. For a while, they had fantasised a relationship based on mutual dysfunction and unrealistic expectations for the future, but then realised they would be drugless and near penniless on discharge. Roger the Rat Boy, scrawny with dirty nails and long lank hair, certainly deserves a reference within the context of criminal vacuity. There are no amusing tales of strokes pulled or personality-based contributions to impressive pub lock-ins involving sex with the landlady or the theft of high value packages. Roger was an excruciating bore who happened to sell drugs; there was nothing redeeming or interesting about him. John, however, had once been a reasonably successful distraction thief with a full-length calfskin leather coat and feather cut hairstyle. Eventually, the drugs were to steal his identity. A dark shadow he never stepped out of.

This particular day was early in the scheme of resourceful ne'er do wells. A greasy hint of breakfast tang lingered in the Transit as it swung into the yard of a provincial auction room. The newly knighted Stealerant had an arrangement whereby, as he unloaded, articles were itemised and given a reserve price, before being taken into the auction room by a brown-coated porter. The reserve prices were then totaled up and he would trouser a cash advance. Exceptional finds would wend their way through due to a seller's necessity for fast cash, as opposed to the London salesrooms where catalogues were king and the payment a distant aspiration that could come unstuck through diligent police detective work. When the final sales of the provincial auction were done and dusted, the cheque would be made out to cash. It was then straight round to the auction house bank, on a bland 1960s shopping precinct with parking provided: *'An excellent arrangement; a pleasure to do business.'* A politeness borne of a temporary affluence, the bundled banknotes: '*How would you like it Sir?*' and '*Oh, twenties and fifties thank you*', along with a fabulous chemical balance that Eddie could nasally taste and flex to feel.

Today, a George III cellaret on Hepplewhite legs, minus the lead lined interior, will be effortlessly converted into mood altering chemicals. The Stealerant and Derby John will indulge exclusively in cat piss smelling amphetamine sulphate, mixed with the amps, to create a particularly fine internal ambience exuding a well-balanced bliss. These pharmaceutical excesses take place in John's unusually low-ceilinged bedsitting-room. The first hit of this concoction almost takes their breath away, finding themselves bent double and sweating. Eventually, this peak plateaus and a heightened sense of wreckedness resumes, complemented by short expletives ending with references to Hades.

In the early hours of the following day at an address dubbed 'Heroin Heights' by local taxi drivers, the Stealerant shoots more speed under a bright bare bulb in a badly converted kitchen equipped with a large porcelain Belfast sink, giraffe-neck taps and water-accelerating rubber nozzles. A muted Next by the Sensational Alex Harvey Band wafts in from the front room. The application of shoplifted Dulux pastel colours gives a cold high-ceiling bathroom a Bonnard shabby chic. Toilet paper is always lacking. In a shuttered front room, a babysitter, paid in Tuinal, sleeps on a once elegant Edwardian drop-end sofa. A turned wooden 1940s lamp is draped with a scarf and a couple of large leather cabin trunks with big brass straps are covered in clothes. The quiet words 'see you later' and a request from a man with a widow's peak using a toothbrush to clean his trainers to '*leave us some cigs.*'

The Transit is dawn-chilled; the engine coughs into life and reverberates through the van as the Stealerant pulls away with a gearbox whine. The scraping steel ashtray squeaks when dragged out, sending a cold shiver down his spine. His cigarette lighter resembles a lipstick holder: a resin heart on the top and bright bands of green and gold. If life had the qualities of a fragrance, the Stealerant would have aspired to a top note of bitter orange peel. The reality is Tabac aftershave with the fusty legacy of provincial auction rooms. In the back of the van, a Paul Masson wine bottle provides a urine receptacle for long distances. A Victorian inlaid writing box, its compartments removed, rests on a heavy gold velvet curtain obtained from the clearance of a gentleman's residence. Wedged against the wheel arch is a fruit box with a collection of curios wrapped in newspaper. All the choice gear went yesterday.

It is now 4.45am on the memorial clock tower, its sandstone witch-deterring finials notionally corroding from the shit of circling seagulls. An empty taxi is parked outside a white broad-fronted Art Deco hotel, next door to the exclusive jeweler that had once repaired the Stealerant's black-faced Omega Seamaster. The Stealerant presses the white china bell of the hotel and Joe the Nightporter appears, nods and unbolts the sweeping revolving door – clean brass and shiny glass. *'Men's evil manners live in brass.'* The subdued reception lights are easy-on-the-eye as they repair to the back residents' bar. Joe serves up and disappears to perform his duties, leaving the Stealerant sharing the bar with the ancient diorama electric crane machine, 'The Novelty Merchantman.' Through an open door, are the sounds of a cistern, water-forced whistling like a call and response from the freshly cleaned Shanks urinal, resplendent with individual glass splash prevention foot screens and a gentle whiff of Jeyes fluid, a product favoured for its hygienic versatility.

Early railway posters line the snug bar, advertising English South Coast destinations: golden beaches, laughing children with buckets and spades and a father smoking a pipe, smiling with his arm round mother's pleated, thick-belted, candy-striped waist. All is fabulous and, as yet, no pink charge sheets in sight. A long plush red buttoned-back bench with a pewter-topped and brass-riveted table separates the guest telephone box from the mechanical, money-fed, glass-encased crane machine. The Stealerant contemplates their respective roles within the hotel. The telephone, in its late 1940s heavy wood, long chrome-handled and glass walk-in cabinet, giving and receiving information, instructions, endearments, perhaps threats and promises. The Novelty Merchantman, a scale model of the bow of a ship in an upright glass cabinet of coffin proportions, with its mechanical jaw dangling from the end of a crane. The circular knob turned to position its jaw over bounty encased in plastic baubles. The weight of the prize dictates the chance of winning, more often than not delivering the public humiliation of a loser. Trophies are Kodak instamatic cameras and watches, capturing the passing of time in numbers and the fixing in photographic images, codifying life.

The Stealerant extends these thoughts to his own existence, deeply detailed as it is. The Dutch speed forces his blood through restricted capillaries, like fingers squeezing the end of a hosepipe. Testicles retract, akin to the undercarriage of a Boeing 747 folding into the belly of the plane, and his tingly-top head buzzes on his hairline, with auto-focus amphetamine eyes giving a peripheral fuzz. He quaffs the cold beer and fires up a cigarette with the lipstick lighter. Thoughts come quicker than a sympathy fuck after a four-year stretch, the scenarios cracking off each other like once beautiful Jaguars and Rover motors entered in stock car races, driven by builder types with busty girlfriends who will train as nurses.

A previous London trip with Booster Paul begins to play like a film in his mind's eye. An auction-bought decade-old Daimler – British racing green and still a bit fusty – a tyre wall perished from long time garage standing while probate was sorted out. A back blowout on the M5 straight into a raining hard shoulder, quickly fixed, no thoughts of 'lucky to be alive.' Back in the comforting carpet and leather, the smell of hot oil and cigarettes. The cassette playing Dire Straits, *Making Movies*; the motor picking up speed as the automatic Borge gearbox drops down, *Tunnel of Love* matching the kick. The Stealerant's dad had once lived on a fairground as a booth fighter. He'd told him disgustedly about some guys with a woman, whose husband was fighting in Korea, having sex in a caravan. Back to the swish and boom into the gloaming, hitting the M4 south of Bristol, tonning the miles to a flat in Ealing for Derek and Clive, Ritalin and a rush.

These spectacular days of criminality, fast chance and heroin sex before the habit fucks you. People do bad things. They break laws moral and criminal. Some of these things are relative to their circumstances and when weighed against decisions of government and institutions add up to nothing, but isolated in a courtroom these individuals will be offered up as the devil incarnate. Is the badness diluted over a wider area of decision-making, the sting so to speak, gently down-graded to an almost unperceivable numbing like a pre-med of Omnopon and Valium?

Ealing: the flat in Ealing. Staying at a bed and breakfast near the common and taking spoons from the dining room, cooking up and leaving them match-sooted on top of the dusty utility wardrobe. Going into an off License the same time as a disheveled individual leaves clutching a blue carrier bag, the type found in trees. The Asian storeowner shakes his head towards the door and comments '*it is sad*', as he hands over a bottle of wine for the Stealerant's breakfast. Overcoated, collar up, a harsh cigarette, cold air on the eyeballs and the dry wine satisfying, loitering in an alley smelling of oil and rubber while the tyre is fixed. Standing on cardboard to avoid clag on the pedals. These were the places where safes were burnt open, where men good with their hands aspired to the ownership of luxury motors they occasionally ring and cousins working as baggage handlers hid things in fortressed lock-ups. These were the days of cash, favours and lock-ins.

Booster Paul had given the Stealerant two pieces of advice. the first: never tell people anything as they usually tell other people to make themselves more interesting. The second: never drive off your head on the A303; it is far better to stick to the M4 slow lane, so if you nod out, you at least have a chance of rolling into the hard shoulder. This last piece of advice was offered after the Stealerant had paid Roger the Rat Boy to drive him up to London to score. Roger had managed to total the motor on the A303 return journey.

Booster Paul's mentor in crime was Lawrence, a man several years older than him and truly immersed in the corruption of small town criminality, with regional tentacles spread through a few prison sentences. Outreach distraction theft in London mansion blocks, signposted by East Sussex

No smoking
in this building

knockers who had leafleted, were called back and preferred a percentage rather than a nicking. Things were never what they seemed to be, the pals in the pub making their entrance but never, ever the reveal, as in the magician's trick. Some of these characters were to unfold like dirty old men preying on pretty hippy birds: snides sussed on acid and given nicknames related to sexual proclivities or personal hygiene. Paul would eventually kill his mentor.

Lawrence and Booster Paul found themselves in the front room of a detached house somewhere off the M25 corridor. Their Transit with its magnetic roofing sign sitting tight up against the overgrown hedge. These leased vans with associated tales of drugs, dementia and domestic arrangements that involved social workers, money hidden in airing cupboards or down the back of washing machines and small parcels of jewellery buried in the garden. The woman in the chair is clearly dead. The two men take the rings from her fingers but not the grandfather clock from the hallway. This will be left for the rapacious relations who will happily share in the spoils of the old woman's death but who never thought to visit in the past six weeks or so. Family members will now have to make do with the obvious semi-portables and paper based bequests. They will never know of the minor artworks, swaddled in the wardrobe, that the two of them converted into heroin and a decade old Daimler.

The killing of Lawrence the mentor was related indirectly to a driving licence, an empty van abandoned near Heathrow and a number of antiques taken from a South Devon manor house. Lawrence claimed his driving license had been stolen by some Brighton Boys and used to hire a van. The police in no uncertain terms explained the sentence for conspiracy usually starts at four years. However, if Lawrence would be willing to state in a court of law that these Brighton geezers had stolen his licence, events could be looked upon in a different light. The Stealerant would never know what else might have been demanded of Lawrence; rumours of police collusion were never proved.

Booster Paul had a friend with a dying dad and a regular supply of Diconal: a very strong opioid analgesic. When crushed and injected, these pills provided an extremely powerful rush. The next day was to be the court appearance, fall to winter, the misery of November and never going gently. Lawrence was a big man and he could be intimidating. He knew this and he could not inject himself. In the dying dad's well-built 1950s council house with a brick shed in the untended garden, Booster Paul shot up a belligerently drunken Lawrence at his own insistence. This was to haunt Paul for the rest of his life.

The years were to roll by. Prime lessons in madness, repeating the same mistakes and expecting different results from these progressively sadder, for all concerned, escapades. The behaviour increasingly extreme, points of self-regulation passed like bold blue motorway service signs. Regrets glanced and dismissed, the Stealerant conned himself with a romanticism based on chemical intake and sentimental music. Reading about a Great Train Robber who hanged himself, in his railway arch lock-up, surrounded by flowers and empty vodka bottles. Then one day seeing a newspaper with a photograph of Anita Pallenberg as an old woman coming out of Waitrose in Chichester. Solitary thoughts involving proclamatory statements, marking the end point of insanity and the beginning of a new adventure without the fear.

Eventually the chassis on the Transit starts to rot, as does the lip of the bonnet and around the headlight pods. On the wing, the cursive chrome word *Custom* cracks on the second syllable and drops. Slow, struggling windscreen wipers flick over the driver's side section of glass pitted with spat steel, the legacy of a bad welding job. The rain kicks up through rusting wheel arches, floor panels flake and the lock on the quarter light breaks. The front is compromised incrementally by the elements, while the passengers are driven to the end of the road on worn steel belt radials. At night, every time the brakes are applied, the interior lights up red. Bail sheets for court appearances correspond with looming MOT tests, road tax and receding affection, in a troubled relationship built on co-dependency, chemicals and theft.

The Stealerant had borne witness to these days and watched them click over on an old school Smith's mechanical odometer. There could be no mileage manipulation in his life, no clocking so to speak; he would now arrive grateful and sober at various destinations where he would never see his old friends.

Booster Paul had once commented to a mutual friend that the Stealerant always seemed to have an exit strategy, something up his sleeve.

A MAN was found dead in public toilets in Torquay, an inquest has been told. There was evidence of drug use inside the locked Union Street toilet cubicle when Paul Lawless, an unemployed 56 year-old single man, was found on Thursday, June 14th. An inquest heard thatfingerprint evidence had been used to identify the deceased, who was born in Watford and lived at Happaway Crescent, Torquay. The inquest heard there were no suspicious circumstances. Toxicology results were still pending and the inquest was adjourned.

The Poodle Faker: Aqualand

Several weeks ago, Clive the Poodle Faker and I had spent over two hours on the phone. We'd been talking about the Marine Spa Ballroom, a magnificent Victorian building that included a swimming pool, spa treatments and restaurants, built when Torquay was the Queen of the English Riviera. Clive told me he could have been a real contender for hosting afternoon tea dances in the fabulous sprung-floor ballroom. He conjured up swooning clientele savouring the spangling piano and a pursed and painted lipped singer crooning into a starburst microphone suspended on springs. It was enough to encourage the vapours and a desire for laudanum and French brandy on the terrace overlooking the Bay.

During the first decade of the 1900s, the Schnee Four Cell Bath was an exclusive feature, used for treating rheumatism and painful joints. A miniature bath for each limb delivered varying electrical charges and the patient could remain fully clothed throughout the procedure. The Marine Spa was to be closed and demolished at the beginning of the 1970s after an eleven-year-old boy (an orphan) was sucked into a barnacle-encrusted filtration pipe in the indoor pool and drowned. I remembered as a boy going to the Marine Spa Tuesday night Leander Swimming Club. I would catch the bus to the harbour, walk along Victoria Parade and up Beacon Hill.

Arches and high ceilings. Clive and I agreed most institutions we attended as youths had something of the ecclesiastical about them and engendered a sense of guilt around the opposite sex. When I was eleven years old, I was caught kissing a girl in a churchyard by the vicar, who told my headmaster. The

headmaster was called Wightman, a man with a bent finger, partial to masticating his own nasal effluvia. He was an ex-cricketer with a two tone Ford Consul. Wightman put me off cricket for life, even though the lead singer of the Rolling Stones is a fan. There was a strong connection between our school and the church, an outdoor swimming pool providing a respite and reoccurring baptism. Years later, it was revealed the kiss and tell vicar had been having relations with a young boy at the church youth club. Also with the boy's mother.

Within the vicinity of the Marine Spa was Aqualand. In a prominent position outside the premises was a huge diving bell with brass-lidded portholes together with a big lifeboat collection box. Not quite delivering the Stingray Supermarionation Gerry Anderson television experience, the dim lighting, treated ozone fragrance, wet floors, humming electrics and purring pumps made it quite exciting in the 1970s. The undulating fake rock fascia with embedded fish tanks and vivariums displayed the exotic and not so exotic local crabs and fish. The predominate colour scheme was purple and green.

Clive had mentioned his Auntie Pamela's connection to Aqualand during September 1970. Auntie Pamela had been onboard a BOAC Vickers VC 10, one of the multiple aircraft hijacked and flown by Palestine Liberation Organization members to Dawson's Field, Jordan. In Auntie's luggage was a Vayangani beach baby turtle she had bought in what was then called Bombay and hidden in a receptacle with a sodden deep-sea sponge. The flight was to London but it was hijacked at a stopover in Bahrain. This was a response to a previously failed hijacking attempt in which a member of the

PLO, Leila Khaled, had been captured. Clive had actually written a poem about this woman. The deal was to release Khaled, who was in British custody, and in return the hijackers would set free the passengers who included Auntie Pamela and the turtle. This situation was resolved through various diplomatic machinations. Leila Khaled was released just after making friends with two female Ealing police officers with whom she was to correspond for many years. Auntie continued her flight to London on another aircraft and at her final destination in Devon she donated the turtle to Aqualand where it lived happily for many years.

In her will, Auntie Pamela left her bungalow to Clive. He later discovered, in the bathroom on a tiled window shelf amongst the shells and pumice stone from the Canary Islands, the turtle-sustaining deep-sea sponge.

Leila
I want to marry a girl from Beirut,
complete with gun and black cheroot,
a threat to my life, a TWA bloodied tarmac wife.
The earth will move under army trucks,
guns to guerrillas coin in the bucks.
We'll walk hand in hand down bomb-cratered streets,
a pram full of grenades it'll be so sweet.

Ammunition box for a bedside table,
some thought to the future always an empty cradle.
I'll bring her presents from London in lead lined bags,
bullets, bangles and duty free fags.

Zero Love 1964

I had a metaphorical girlfriend – let's call her Eva – who meant the world to me. On an emotional level, I invested heavily in this woman and sometimes on impulse bought expensive items that I thought would make me more appealing to her. I loved the idea of Eva; she was beautifully proportioned in a Vargas stylised fashion; she could have been painted on a bomber.

Eva's father was a mean, violent bastard, slow with his exaggerated pronunciation but quick with his hands. He would get agitated listening to the radio. It was almost like the radio signals had a direct feed on his neurons and if you broke that feed, he would lash out.

He hit her. On the radio, Sonny Liston was fighting Cassius Clay at Lewiston, Maine, 25th May 1964. It was a record low attendance for a world heavyweight title fight. As Liston was falling, he hit her twice in rapid succession. There was a long count in the Liston/Clay fight. He hit her. She fell back against a glass table, the glass cracked, the inside of her leg offered the artery and the glass welcomed it. Liston gained ten seconds. He got up, Eva didn't.

I found myself staring at inanimate objects, a form of comforting mesmerism, a habit I have never broken. There was a motorcycle, a low rider, called an Indian. The profile of an Indian chieftain was painted on the gas tank; riding in a hard rain tears would pearl across the face. The Indian had a V-twin engine, which meant the pistons pumped in line, one to the front and one to the rear, driving you forward, driving you away from.

I rode to Las Vegas, through Death Valley, the shimmering desert heat and lunar cold night, with one of Eva's seamed stockings over the air filter. I learnt the motorcycle of choice on the wall of death is the Indian.

That World

'That world! These days, it's all been erased and they've rolled it up like a scroll and put it away somewhere. Yes, I can touch it with my fingers. But where is it?'

Denis Johnson – *Jesus' Son*

For Leon, the obvious legacy of cystic fibrosis was a Barnacle Bill barrel-chest that his spindly arms were attached to like a mismatched *Action Man*. His father Chris, with corresponding physical features, carried the gene from his side but had skipped the debilitating condition. Chris worked mostly two weeks on, two weeks off, on oil rigs in the Forties region of the North Sea and tried to have an interest in photography when he hadn't pawned his camera for drugs at the fag end of the fortnightly stint.

Posh and Becks: her with the sulky resting bitch face, him with the suave speed-boated profile, portrayed a perfect family unit, beautiful, healthy and fabulously rich. Contrastingly, Leon's family knew nothing but a self-induced poverty, due to bad decisions with occasional government agency interventions around incriminating statements and possible care orders. The limbo and drama of petty criminality subsidised by sickness benefit, stolen jewelry and traded methadone, accrued during uninterrupted periods of drug dealing.

Leon's meals, Birdseye traditional beef in home-style gravy, stacked up in the freezer, but he was kept out of the kitchen while the adults cooked up. *Blue Velvet* kisses after a good hit, firing up a cigarette with part of the filter missing. Spoon soot smudged melamine surfaces; pop tarts and coloured chrome collared Bic lighters. Looking out across the way through the metal-framed window, past outhouses and washing lines no one ever used, to newer blocks, built over demolished prefabs.

Maybe that's the thing about gear, the environment doesn't really matter. It creates a space of your own, like a viewing platform somewhere in an emotional Switzerland. But not a Switzerland David Bowie lived in or where the ghost of Charlie Chaplin wanders.

Leon's pancreas did not make enough enzymes and, as a consequence, he had to take a prescriptive medication called Creon that enabled him to digest food. Blond and elfin, he would play on the floor, making loud *tshush, tshush* expellations while smashing Transformer toys into each other, looking up to see if anyone noticed. His violent fantasies took place on a booze and ash-clagged 1970s swirled carpet inherited from the catalogue selection of a previous tenant. There was also his bedwetting issue – the rubber sheet emitted a loud buzzing sound when moisture came into contact with it. It was almost as if Leon was constantly punished for things he had no power over.

Janet, his mother, had always had a penchant for reggae, the bass riff and boom a constant soundtrack in the fag-fugged flat. She would light up a joint first thing in the morning – the makings, blue skins and resin block kept in a brass Princess Mary WWI Christmas tin on a carved Indian side table with the requisite scarf draped lamp ala Keith Richards traveling circus. Chasing smack through a lack of veins, occasional freebase pre-crack days, with the accompanying tea bag and ammonia palaver, drinking Red Stripe, Pussers Rum and rarely eating. There was something almost uncool about eating. Bacofoil, as opposed to the economy alternatives, did not prevent the cancer later.

Janet's Scottish mother was a staunch born again Christian who had made a point of telling none of Janet's old friends how serious the situation was. On her hospital deathbed, Janet's mother persuaded her to accept Jesus into her life. I dwelt on this fact, considering just how lonely and frightened she would have been. Prior to her terminal illness, Janet had moved into a narrow house with a small kitchen in a city with a sympathetic drug agency, enabling a half-life on a maintenance prescription. Death, the ultimate geographical – even Houdini didn't get a word back. Chris, Leon's dad, was to die of stomach cancer two months before Janet; they had been separated for many years.

I have often thought of Leon, the unfairness of his circumstances. I remember one summer when he was on the front page of the local paper – I think he was about 12 at the time. He had been horribly stung by a nest of wasps, near a solitary tree outside his home.

Sometime after Janet's death, I met Leon. He was about 22 by then. It was December and we went for a pizza near the cathedral; I had just bought a copy of Jonathan Frazens' *The Corrections*. I gave Leon £20 for Christmas. I knew he was speeding, as he was exceptionally strident in his conversation. People were looking at our table but that didn't bother me; what bothered me was the fact that I was useless. I could give him my number but I couldn't put anything right. I knew as I listened to him, to what I can't remember now, that these weren't the good old days anymore and I somehow felt complicit in contributing to his damaged childhood.

The only respite Leon ever really got from smoke was at school or in the beer gardens of pubs with names like The Banner Cross or The Royal Standard, or when things got so bad he was treated in hospital. 'Treated' being the operative word. His breathing equipment had been compromised from birth and endangered on a daily basis. Selfishness and ignorance. . .there was plenty to go round. In the twelve-step recovery program there is a specific step, step nine, when an individual makes direct amends to anyone who has been harmed by their behaviour. Leon was due an abundance of amends: witnessing a friend of his mothers' being dragged from the room and driven to a cash point, not before getting their stash of heroin into the chinchilla cage. The perpetuator of this violence was to be stabbed by Booster Paul a few years later and questioned, spittle splattered, eye-to-eye, for three minutes with a blade in him. All over a stolen microwave that was sold to a fish and chip shop for a tenner.

There was a time during the late 1980s when I was in London with Janet, Leon and my then girlfriend Viv. We were staying in a maisonette on Cable Street that was rented to a guy who sold apartments within the dockland developments, before the *Long Good Friday*. The memory of this area was gaunt, dark with echoing pigeon sounding tunnels, clanking blues-beat bridges, dripping stone arches and steel plated lock ups. You could almost hear the hobnails on the cobbles ringing out in the gloaming, hissing gas fires

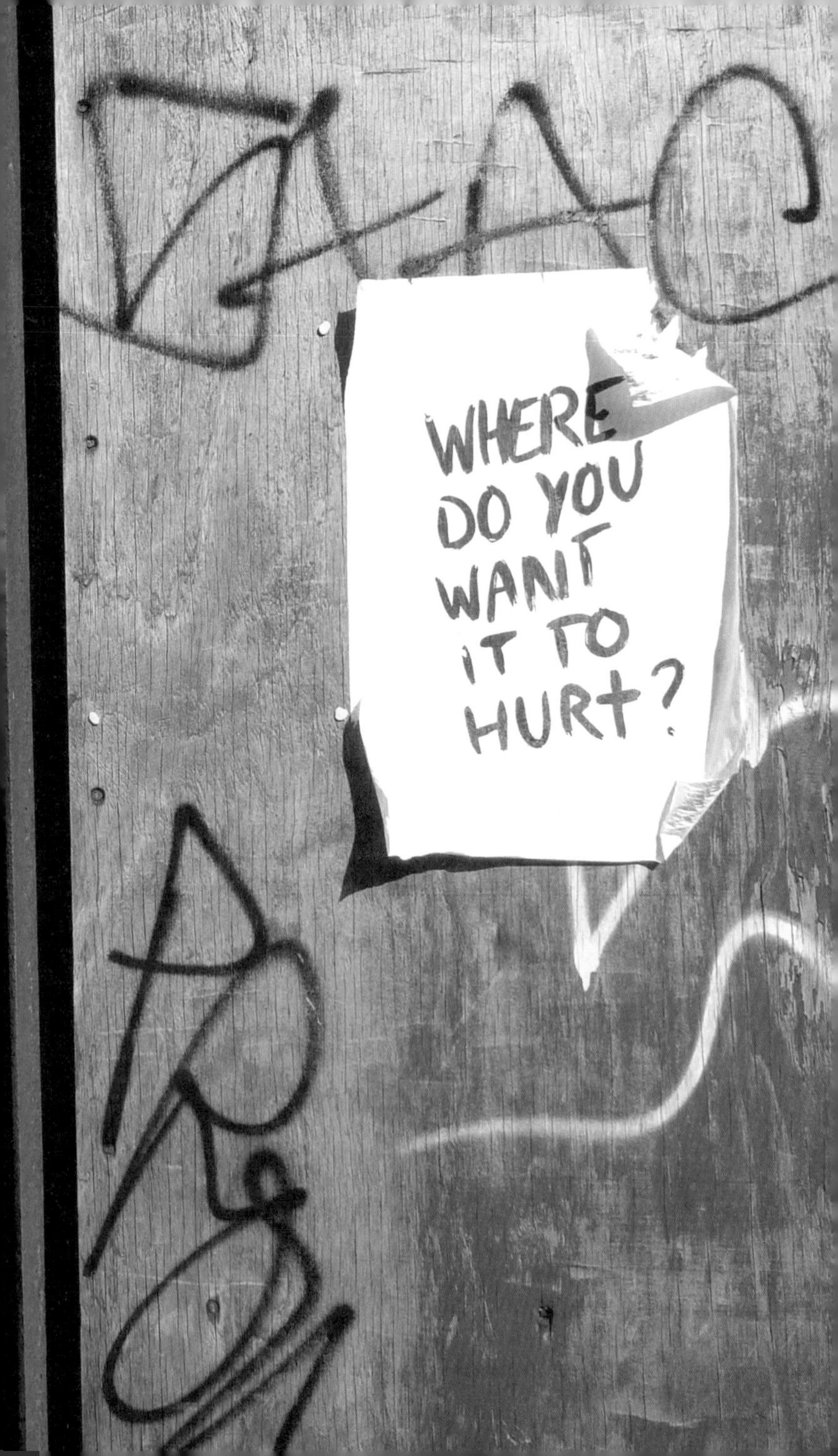
WHERE DO YOU WANT IT TO HURT?

and claggy sweat-stinking overcoats covering the sort of violence that really breaks things.

We had to go to the Out Patients Department at the London Hospital in Whitechapel to get Leon some medication. There was a junction on Cable Street and, as we approached it, two cars loudly collided. One sped away leaving the other battered, steaming and beaten. While we waited for the medicine, Viv, wearing heroin chic and Chloe perfume, gave me a driving license with a staggeringly easy signature. Some months later, I hired a motor from a rental firm in Oxford; near the premises was a fiberglass shark tail sticking out of the roof of a terraced house. I remembered the shark because it was controversial. I knew nothing at that time about conceptual art, but I liked the shark and placed it into my arty memory bank, along with Merce Cunningham on a black and white television in a bedroom overlooking Cockington meadow, Torquay. Several credit cards and a haircut later, stopping for fuel in the Somerset flatlands, a hitch-hiker asked – as the engine tinked – if it was a hire car. A few years later, I heard John Cooper Clarke perform one of his poems, *Hire Car*, and dedicate it to his pal, a gardening writer called Martin Newell.

Time: the distance, the space and – always for me, when conscious of it – the parallels. What was my dad doing while I was waiting with Janet and Viv? What would he have said if he had walked in then, right then into that hospital waiting room? He would probably have made reference to when he had boxed in the area, beating one of the Burns brothers from the East End. My dad had been a journeyman professional fighter, ranked fifth in the UK welterweight division in 1955: an era of hungry fighters. I was a waster, drawn to darkness through a lack of ambition, or maybe opportunity, who knows.

Leon never had a choice. His illness gave Janet another identity apart from drug addict – the mother of a sick boy. Did one follow the other or was it the other way around? Leon was sometimes the deflection, the reason for writing a statement against a dealer and the threat of the care order. In all this shame and misery, the next hit and minor victory at an auction room made it all pathetically worthwhile. I wondered if anyone really cared outside the chemical induced emotions. What really went on with Janet and Leon when the gear ran out but his illness persisted?

I did have moments with my dad: shared moments, drinking times. One Sunday afternoon, we were between pubs in an Austin 1100 that had been lost in a card game. Simon and Garfunkel were singing *A Most Peculiar Man* on the eight track and my dad turned to me and told me how much the song reminded him of me. A few miles up the road, we ran out of petrol and he tasked me to go and get some while he waited with the motor. I later realised the record was about someone who commits suicide.

You can pick your friends but you can't pick your family.

The Poodle Faker: Passing Points

'Did you know there are more roads in the county of Devon than there are in the whole of Belgium?' Clive the Poodle Faker is in full flow and, without taking a breath, continues, *'I can totally relate to the character of Bunny who Bill Murray plays in the film Ed Wood. Do you remember the scene where there is a wrap party for 'Bride of the Atom' in a meatpacking factory and one of the cast, a Scandinavian wrestler type asked Bunny how his trip to Mexico went? Bunny tells a tale of absolute horror, and then theatrically with a sweep of his hand directs their gaze to a mariachi ensemble dressed in silver studded charro outfits performing behind him. He then tearfully chokes, 'If it wasn't for these men I don't know how I would have survived.'* Clive teases a potted purple African violet and resumes his tale of emotional salvation: *'The country lanes of Devon saved my life – if it wasn't for those lanes, my lanes of unconditional love, I don't know how I would have survived.'*

We are standing in an enormous garden centre. Clive has a trolley in front of him; a pair of 'Big Hands' nestles together with plant food for lemon trees, a premium watering can with a brass rose and a plastic container of bird feed fat balls. I ask him again what happened in the lanes.

Clive folds his arms and sort of shivers; I can see he's not comfortable. *'Do you remember my last Barbara, the proud possessor of the Isadora Duncan scarf remnant?'* Clive refers to all his women friends as 'Barbaras', a term of very special affection, regardless of their real names. *'She drove off in a Topaz Mist, Nissan Figaro leaving me sans sou'wester on wet and windy Thurlestone beach. This occurred around the time when David Bowie released The Next Day album – a significant moment for me as I had seen Bowie live in April 1972 at the Plymouth Guild Hall and she knew this. Sudden and shocking, like being bitten. Scorpio rising, Arab Springs. I don't know what it's all about sometimes. Pessimistically, I embrace a final phase through break-ups such as this, marking my own stories between the pillars in the temple of my mortality. I concluded that Barbara was driven to reinvention and Thurlestone beach was her nadir. I found the parting devastating. I totally lost my appetite, I couldn't sleep and high-level dusting was simply out of the question due to my loss of balance. There was only one distraction that worked and this was driving through the country lanes, and importantly it was the stopping, the waiting in the passing points.'*

An aproned assistant carrying an elaborately fronded plant nods at Clive as he passes by. '*I do love coming here; it almost provides an emotional Switzerland for me.*' I notice Clive is wearing a beautiful silk cravat, with little pheasants on it, the type that is backed with cotton to keep the neck cool and prevent slippage. Clive continues:

'*I have developed an exceedingly good knowledge of the country lanes in South Devon: hedge height, road girth, the position of salt bins, different gates such as the swan neck, spindle top, picket, the classic flat top five-bar and the locations of farmhouse cream teas. For many years there was a huge white concrete teapot on the gatepost of a house between Newton Abbot and Totnes. It reminded me of my Auntie Evelyn, a habitual London-based tea drinker and housekeeper to the Oppenheimers. I always had a flask with me as I savoured my vehicular solitude. The tea a mixture of Earl Grey and Darjeeling, my choice of biscuit the round fluted Waitrose fruit shortcake. Occasionally there was the issue of biscuit morsels, this I addressed with my Sheffield silver Silent Butler crumb-catcher. Auntie Pamela had lost the brush to this years ago. It looked like a small bed warming pan and I found it exceedingly comforting panned across my lap as I sipped and nibbled.*

Music was also a comfort; Benjamin Smoke a particular favourite. I would steer my old Volvo with tears in my eyes as he sang, well sort of spoke, a number called 'Friends.' I had never been a great mixer and it is predominantly the company of females I prefer. However, at a distance and encased in their cars I found I was quite happy to wave at anybody. I discovered that if I pulled in to allow other vehicles to pass, I was rewarded with waves of gratitude and sometimes accompanied smiles. My world changed, I felt better about myself and certainly more benevolent toward humanity as a whole. I envisaged my own mariachi ensemble, elevated on an elaborate podium playing to me from a passing point as I drove through a favourite tree arched lane; I would wave like a fireman in 'Blue Velvet.'

We both get up and walk to the cafeteria. I order us a pot of tea and a couple of slices of heavy fruit laden moist bread pudding with the crunchy crust. Our table overlooks the resin and plaster water features that appear to draw people with horned fetish necklaces and colourful woven wrist-bands. I notice a number of balding men with ponytails. Electric wheelchairs glide between the aisles of bubbling aeration, with front baskets holding wet wipes and dangling mascot gifts from grandchildren and serving soldiers.

'*I have experienced heartbreak before you know. Veronica, an early Barbara, ran an industrial cleaning company during the late 1980s in the docklands. She had blue hair; it was an expression of a style that she described as 'Imperial Punk', homage to Quentin Crisp. Quentin has always inspired me through his self-belief and his emigration to America aged 73. Just consider for a moment, starting again at 73 years old. Her mother had been a seamstress for the royal family and kept trunks full of discarded royal lingerie and linen.*' Clive's voice had gone up a register, but it was good to see him on form and I always thoroughly enjoyed his entertainments. He wiped his brow with a silk handkerchief and cathedraled his hands: '*It is always affaires de Coeur that have brought me to the brink, to the very precipice of hopeless despair. I used to compliantly nod to the Goethe quote: 'What doesn't kill us makes us stronger', but heartbreak depleted my reserves.*'

'*I remember visiting a hotel near Slapton Sands in South Devon. It was at the end of a narrow coastal lane with extremely sparse passing points. My first impressions were of a tall Victorian vicarage transposed from Scarborough. The hotel itself had seen better days, it had an air of genteel shabbiness: window frames with flaking paint and blown plaster on the exterior. The high narrow double doors of the main entrance had etched glass panels that rattled and their brass handle collars were missing. The bar was more of an old steel frame conservatory, probably called the orangery fifty years ago, with fraying Lloyd Loom and bamboo two-seater settees. A warped wooden trellis had plastic oranges and lemons intertwined with an occasional dusty ivy leaf. The details were important to me and I found mesmerising comfort in this display of architectural and domestic decay.*

A White Horse whisky ice bucket and a long-emptied Schweppes soda siphon sat on the bar with a mismatch of faded bar towels. In pride of place was a signed photograph of the 1950s Irish chanteuse Ruby Murray. I'd known Ruby many years ago. She introduced me to the work of Lenny Bruce and lent me an album of Edith Piaf. I like to think my eye for detail is inherited from my Auntie Pamela; you know she worked with the code breakers at Bletchley Park during the war. She would have particularly liked the plastic Babycham fawn imprisoned in the empty cigar display case.

The incongruous sight of a rusting skeletal yellow industrial crane, with an over-sized lucky dip bucket, rudely disturbed the coastal view in this area of outstanding natural beauty. I enquired as to the presence of this heavy machinery and it transpired the owner had been fighting an ongoing war with the cliff erosion for the past twenty years or so. He would use the crane at low tide to deposit rubble at the base of the cliff. This action, which became his obsession, was at the expense of the hotel. All the energy and resources he was pouring in diverted him away from any necessary maintenance work and he was fighting a battle he could not win. I later discovered he died of a heart attack in the bar, pulling the handle on a fruit machine. Try as I might, I could never find this hotel again.'

We enter a space of mutual quietude and respectful contemplation, as I think carefully about what Clive has said. I feel I owe him an intelligent response, as opposed to glib agreement. I remember when I first met Clive several years earlier at his late Auntie Pamela's bungalow, he emanated an aura of loneliness, not intentionally but there was an aspect of the stoic smiling through the tears – a hint of Lawrence Oliver in *The Entertainer* but without the nasty sentiment.

May it Pass Quickly

Bad Penny was floaty in scarves that doubled as tourniquets, turning up like a Poundshop Stevie Nicks, all festive and restless with sausagey fingers from shooting in her hands. She would bring along an older boyfriend called Smarty, his bottle-thick round glasses and corkscrew hair barely disguising this casualty of the 1960s, who remembered the golden days of NHS dry amps collected from the midnight Boots on Piccadilly.

Bad Penny's mother was the resident matron of a local authority nursing home, with a strong work ethic and the alcoholic disposition of an ex-army wife, who remembered the OMO washing powder boxes on windowsills indicating Old Man Out. Bad Penny was home for the Brompton Cocktail rather than the turkey and tinsel. Like a military campaign, manoeuvres would be put in place to liberate the keys of the DDA cabinet, thus enabling an unrushed selection of an alternative Quality Street. Resident consequences were not a consideration. The Christmas Eve party provided the distraction as the staff all hailed the matron.

Christmas Day 1973 would be spent under the same roof, yet with different influences. The nodding narcotised and the alcoholic dramatics crashing on Boxing Day with the recognition that all is not well.

The Denzel Dance Trois Parter
Changing Direction
WORK

Denzel tried to notice everything, sometimes closing one eye and imagining that his glasses were a director's viewfinder, similar to one of those telescope looking things they use in films. It was all about films for Denzel; he had always wanted to be in films, preferably on the directing side. The glamour of the film industry made him occasionally sigh out loud and dwelling on his self-projected involvement would keep him awake until the hour of the clanking ghost milk float.

Sometimes Denzel noticed too much, bordering on the obsessive. Because of this, he would become concerned that others had noticed as well and this trait would run relentlessly through everything: preening in the mirror, checking for lint on his lapels, the cleanliness of his shoes. Denzel was 'on' from the moment he rose. An exceptionally serious concern was his spectacle selection, recognising that the public expected him to look his best. Spectacle comparisons were drawn prior to making his choice, a choice he would have to live with for at least a year under National Health Service, tax credit regulations – eligible because of his zero hour, minimum wage status.

Denzel kept his hours up through persistent hard work, taking all the 5.00 am starts that nobody wanted. The lonely cold mornings of rushed ablutions in a sometimes seemingly friendless bastard city that rinsed the choicest years out of you if you didn't stay ahead of the wash. Denzel had cut out and wall mounted photographs from film industry journals of spectacle-wearing directors he respected, to enable a narrowing down of the selection process. He noticed the late Theo

Angelopoulos, an esteemed Greek filmmaker, wore discreet wire-framed spectacles, whereas Martin Scorsese, the American, opted for heavy black frames. These two were the main contenders and he felt a compromise was necessary. A trip to the new Foyles Bookshop on Charing Cross Road on his day off, for an indulgent copy of monthly *Sight & Sound*, nailed the whole issue. On the second floor fiction section, he noticed an employee, whose name badge read Patrick, was wearing a pair of glasses similar to a style worn by the *Howl* poet Alan Ginsberg. Denzel decided to really push the boat out and purchased a copy of *How To Read a Film* by James Monaco and asked Patrick where he had obtained his glasses. It transpired he had bought them at a very reasonable price through a contact lens deal at Specsavers.

The spectacle selection was almost on par with the William H. Macy orthodontics scene in the 1999 American film *Magnolia*. His character, Donny, is working at a dead-end job but whilst being fitted for expensive braces finds himself the centre of attention, his visage illuminated like a movie star under surgery lights. Denzel had been relishing his visit to the optician for a while. It was just a little time when someone would care about him in this city.

Denzel's soul-destroying job necessitated the implementation of elaborate coping skills in order to keep his dreams burning as bright as a 1937 Paramount City Klieg spotlight. He likened his position as Manager at the Paddington Station outlet of Mister Crusties to krokodil addiction – krokodil being a flesh eating street drug from Russia. Denzel had watched a Vice internet documentary about this drug, made from painkillers and adulterated with chemicals such as petrol and sulphur. Its legacy leaves skin looking like crocodile hide before the affected limb rots and falls off. Denzel recognised that his dire toil could corrode his esprit, eat his very soul and cause his creativity to dissipate in the cloying stink of old fat and fear-based corporate wisdom pushed by the company: *'Denzel you need to think about your future and the opportunities this company can offer....'*

Mister Crusties is a converted sub-standard American Airstream caravan affair, where the service industry assistant is a reluctant star with nowhere to hide. A drop-down side displays a gathering of grafters wishing they were somewhere else. A group portrait in situ would not look out of place in a Kodak chrome Martin Parr photo feature. However, there exists a quiet desperation more suited to a Bill Brandt black and white. The staff are mostly Asians and central Europeans, each with their accompanying rituals, beliefs and standards of education achieved and aspired. Whilst the Muslim guys can only butter the bacon rolls, they pester a Spanish boy to use his bedsit for romantic dalliances. This banter passes the time as customers unwittingly walk in and out of numerous fantasies involving web browsed lingerie and heavy petting.

At any one time, there are up to five people in this confined space with the possibility of visiting company personnel. To run this operation smoothly, a manager is required, closely followed by an assistant manager; you cannot overlook a supervisor and there is a good chance a regional manager will appear – *just like that.* Lesser-spotted individuals are the district manager, representatives from the HR department and the CEO. Denzel, a man of detail who prided himself on his appearance, punctuality and pronunciation, was mortified when a female operations manager came to the shop and commented that the logo on his t-shirt was faded and he should get a new one.

Denzel Dance is a man with a strategy, a maker of lists on a Charles Lindbergh scale; minutia is king in his detailed world. Den, as his team of comestible collaborators know him, is always devising scenarios where well known directors order something in a cool manner but notice him in profile and excitedly offer him a walk-on part in a big budget production. This is all wishful thinking, feeding into the scene described by William Burroughs in his book *Junkie*, where the ne'er-do-well is always waiting for the fixer to walk into in the 42nd Street bar and say: *'you're the guy I need on my next job'*. Denzel was aware that Lana Turner was never discovered waitressing in Schwab's the Hollywood drugstore and that it was a studio-spawned urban myth.

REST

Denzel was a married man and the marriage was stultifyingly unhappy, the realisation that there are expectations and there is reality. Lindsay and Denzel had met on a Post Graduate Certificate of Education university course. They had both been attracted by the bursary, alongside the opportunity to validate an arts degree with a teaching qualification, whilst playing for time in the fun house of academia. Their resultant child, monikered Major, a name more fitting for a Labrador, seemingly channeled the parents' mutual malevolent discontentment.

Lindsay aspired to the late Victorian and early Edwardian bow-fronted town houses and terraces of 'Nappy Valley', the ones with the fussy ornate plasterwork usually on an arch in the hallway, at Lavender Sweep and Clapham Junction, where dedicated shops sell cute baby accessories and big pushchairs, their fifty quid parasols blocking the pavements outside fragrant delicatessens and specialist teashops.

However, this was not possible due to a number of factors dictated by money, hard luck and a direct result of their own lack of motivation masquerading as *c'est la vie*. One suspects there were extremely disappointing familial financial expectations on both sides of this relationship that never matured. The rich American relations who never came through after frequent boasts involving Lake Tahoe and European tours.

Denzel and his family were to be located in a featureless fronted block of flats that were neither here nor there in the London location stakes: ex local authority and now mostly buy-to-let with a number of elderly council tenants still in residence. It was the type of building that had spitting prohibition signs in the hallways and that sweet cloying stink of decomposition lagging the large industrial bins in the communal spaces under the stairwells. Lindsay insisted on using real terry toweling nappy squares but she discovered they were useless at distributing the wetness produced by baby Major and leaked unless they had been washed before use to increase their absorbency. These were part of the real life lessons to be learnt, one being the law of the nappy. A nappy will reach its maximum absorbency after about 6 washes, but it is worth washing at least 2-3 times as a minimum before first use.

Denzel had made notes of cleaning comparisons and detailed possible enhancement techniques. The rituals were hell: the relentless washing along with the metal-framed windows, the constantly breaking voodooed tumble drier and the condensation that you didn't have the energy to finger-draw a smiley face in. The cracking, blistering putty withering in the metal frames, like the receding affection within the relationship. These windows, as part of a European decent homes directive, would soon be replaced with UPVC double glazed units. A fresh start for someone else.

The close proximity of others, with their noises and smells – cooking and personal – and the communal hallways cluttered with possessions, bikes, prams, small broken pieces of furniture, served as a constant reminder of the splendid isolation money can buy. The boomy muffled commentary of the downstairs deaf septuagenarian neighbours' radio, the metre always sounding like 1970s football results. The flat above was sublet to an undulating number of Argentinean restaurant workers whose love for good steak was only exceeded by their passion for partying. Antics would usually start around Thursday night and end in the early hours of Sunday morning. The clacking high heels on the concrete steps, fast squeaking trainers, laughter, doors slamming and excited talk segueing to sensual modulation and bags clanking with bottles. The soundscape of a place neither Denzel nor his wife visited anymore.

Of course, none of the above is true; it is just an elaborate fiction created by Denzel, a personification of a dystopian agony he had manufactured to justify his inclusion in the world of the tortured artist. It needs to be revealed that Denzel is of Greek descent on his father's side, his mother being Welsh. Therefore, in the fabulous tradition of Greek tragedy, there must be a challenge, a task so improbable that mythological assistance will be required. As if it wasn't hard enough already, he made relentless job applications to a prestigious London-based cinema chain that included Lindsay Duncan and Bill Nighy amongst its regular clientele. His library printed CVs were handed in with regular dedication on his days off and a ritualistic extravagant sesame seed bar was purchased at the health food shop on Piccadilly, along with the occasional organic – of course – fig.

Whilst handing in a CV to an attractive well spoken refined young lady – a possible Chichester exile – at the box office one afternoon, he was extremely aware of his fingers taking on the appearance of Jesse Eisenberg's in a particular scene of the film *Night Moves*: knuckled with long spindly digits. Denzel was worried that he might whiff of Mister Crusties as he waited in the foyer enveloped by bespoke fragrances, conscious of his thin worn soles on the muffling carpet. Oh to be part of this gentile working environment, a compensation for his cramped and damp subterranean room with a shared toilet and fungus-incubating bathroom on Caledonian Road that his mother would occasionally help him clean, especially when he'd had a bad stomach through nerves or diet. All of this compounded the truth of his lonely existence but reinforced his determination.

PLAY AWAY

There does feature within Denzel's life, a Birkenstock sandaled self-styled Canadian guru who cultivates a following of emotionally castrated males and pseudo spiritual vicious females of a certain age. Denzel had been warned with passionate profanity by his Greek Cypriot barber about taking advice from a man who had his photograph manipulated in a way that depicted a halo of light around his head. Some months later in the news, it was reported that Russell Brand courted controversy by having a similar image on a world tour poster and thus had to cancel much of the Middle East.

Attending one of the Guru's cash on the door seminars, Denzel had asked a question from the open floor, relating to personal growth and the achievement of individual goals. The receding blonde haired bearded guru sat cross-legged and inanely smiling, playing the trusty number of power in silence. Denzel just nodded conspiratorially like an acid casualty 'getting it.' These questionable 'providing a service not hurting anyone' gurus were the sort to end up selling Oriental rugs in places like Bath, claiming dubious ethical goodwill and charitable status. This was usually after failing with an esoteric bookshop with a sideline in legal highs in some hostel-raddled South Coast resort. The Guru offered, on a sliding scale, different levels of spiritual attainment: a business model Denzel thought was possibly borrowed from John jet-pilot Travolta's church organisation, referencing *The Master*, starring the late Philip Seymour Hoffman. Denzel noted all this in his 'for' and 'against' list he had started to compile in an attempt to anchor himself. Why were the Guru's acolytes so happy, fragrant and dazzle toothed – particularly the women? The types who were never seen at an early morning plastic sloping-seat bus stop.

Denzel found himself dwelling more and more. Particularly on greed and glasses. This specific fixation had been ignited during a chance encounter in a church hall kitchen while attending one of his spiritual seminars. Denzel was pouring tea for himself and another attendee when he happened to comment on his tan. The bronzed man started to explain how he and his wife had just come back from Cadiz, where they had met many years ago and were now celebrating their 20-year wedding anniversary. He pulled out his mobile phone and started showing Denzel photographs, pointing out one particular street scene with workmen in fluorescent jackets, remarking how hard they were working under a Spanish sun. It was then that Denzel heard the obese financier, who had slid into their private moment, comment cynically: '*Yes, that's what a recession does*.' He said it in a way that was almost celebratory. The double-decaded husband smiled, put his phone in his pocket and went back to the main hall.

Denzel studied the engorged moneyman eating a chocolate digestive with one paw and pouring tea with the other. He had been briefly introduced to this man who worked in the City, but it had left Denzel with the feeling that he was looking over his shoulder for someone more interesting. The moneyman had something of Billy Bunter about him; expensive tailoring could not disguise his fattened veal calf corpulence. The dark suit, white shirt collar fighting with the puffy neck, a striped silk tie and straining red braces, the pinkie finger signet ring, chunky gold cufflinks and a wafer thin watch: *'Just one more After Eight Sir?'* The crowning glory: his brilliantine baby hair topping off the rosy chubby cheeks all framed by white-rimmed oval spectacles.

Denzel started to faze, like a digital station on a Bose radio. This was his eye for detail, his self-obsession and his paradoxical desire to be in films – an industry so obviously self aware – was a modern condition, slipped in with electricity and George Formby.

After leaving the venue, there was an element of flâneuring before Denzel found himself in the oasis of Postman's Park, near the brutalist Barbican Estate, reading wall-mounted Doulton tablets describing deeds of self-sacrifice. The trying to make sense of it all, the significantly intruding happy childhood memories and the walk on and walk off gallery of characters each providing Denzel with filmic references to responses he had carried and employed throughout his life so far.

The Thoughts that Sustain Us . . .

Louise, sitting on her needlepoint prisoner-stitched cushion, steers the little black car past Toynbee Hall on Commercial Street, E1 where the Atlantic girl-flier Amelia Earhart had once been fêted. She passes in close proximity to Carter House, built in 1928, set back on the Holland Estate opposite the Jewish Soup Kitchen.

Pointing the shiny nose of her German motor toward the A406, Louise proceeds to hold her nerve until the M25 junction where she joins the M4 for a clear run home, the steady diesel thrum, to the land of her birth. The air is crisp as frozen linen and the stars are out tonight as she crosses the Severn Bridge, on past the towering Celtic Manor and the dragon-eyed fire of Port Talbot steel works. Gwasanaethau calls to her for coffee but the choir of the river by Awelfro pulls harder.

A Dutch-built Fokker Friendship airplane touched down in the bay of Burry Port, South Wales on the 17 June 1928, a flight of twenty hours and forty minutes. Wilmer Stultz was the pilot and Louis Gordon the co-pilot and mechanic. On this occasion Amelia Earhart was tasked to keep the flight log.

Louise turns off by the Jerusalem Chapel, twisty steep and home. A quiet committee waits in the garden, cats and owls and small scurrying things anticipating a warm chimney wall.

. . . And the Things that Comfort

During the Second World War Miss Shepherd used to drive ambulances in Plymouth. A quarter of a century later, while lodging in Torquay, she sewed back on the amber-eyed, ginger head of my teddy bear the wrong way round, strengthening the thread with candle wax. I knew she had witnessed the darkness of the human soul, so I never uttered a word. I have always cherished that bear.

As I evolved into a bachelor adult I realised many of my friends, pairing off in partnerships, had other people to talk to. Their selective telephones banished me, like a pauper from the Bugatti Boutique in Brompton Road, Knightsbridge.

I have watched with sadness whimsical bear-celebritys wax and wane, from the titled, affected associations of Brideshead Revisited to Sir John Betjeman and the collectible button-eared Steiff's of the rapacious *Antiques Roadshow*.

This Christmas my bear shall provide, as always, a comfort. I will hold his padded foot, rough as the canvas of a 1940s hospital stretcher, while watching the Queen's speech.